HUNTER SCHOOL

"In the indigenous literary firmament, Sakinu has always been one of our most important stars. His stories of growing up a Paiwan boy are engaging and environmentally conscious, and his simple wisdom will take your breath away. He may not be known in New York, London, Paris, or Milan, but his generosity, insight, and forgiveness make him one of the most important writers in the world."

—WITI IHIMAERA
Author of *The Whale Rider*

"Sakinu's work shares with the world an aspect of Taiwan that has been overlooked, namely its rich indigenous culture and history as well as the inner world of a charismatic tribal leader and teacher whose deep connection to the primordial source of our consciousness helps bring us back to our natural state of wellbeing."

—CINDY THEIL
Producer of *The Sage Hunter*, a film based on Sakinu Ahronglong's life

"Sakinu's work does not just make you smile – in it you can also perceive the allure of the alpine wilderness and the responses the Paiwan people have evolved in this wilderness."

—WU MING-YI

Author of *The Stolen Bicycle*, listed for the 2018 Man Booker International Prize

"*Hunter School* is an important addition to the still small but growing corpus of Taiwan's indigenous writing in English translation. Ably and lovingly translated by Darryl Sterk, the collection of tales, in which the author assays what it means to be Paiwan in contemporary Taiwan, is now available to the English-speaking reader and should not be missed."

—JOHN BALCOM

Award-winning translator of Chinese literature, philosophy, and children's books

HUNTER SCHOOL

Sakinu Ahronglong

Translated from Mandarin by
Darryl Sterk

Honford
Star

This translation first published by Honford Star 2020
honfordstar.com
© Sakinu Ahronglong 1998
Translation copyright © Darryl Sterk 2020

ISBN (paperback): 978-1-9997912-8-5
ISBN (ebook): 978-1-9997912-9-2
A catalogue record for this book is available from the British Library.
Cover illustration by Chia-Chi Yu

Printed and bound in Paju, South Korea

Sponsored by the Ministry of Culture, Republic of China (Taiwan)

CONTENTS

RECLAIMING WHAT WAS LOST

Introduction

Ever since I was a boy, I've seen my Paiwan tribespeople inundated by society, carried away in the flood. Growing up, I witnessed members of my tribe getting eaten away by reality, even swallowed whole. Reality's pursuit is relentless, while tradition has receded from us, leaving us helpless and indecisive, leaving wounds in our hearts – in our innermost worlds. The reality is that our villages have been invaded by foreign culture, which has fragmented the tribal social structure and deprived us of the totemic tattoos that adorned the bodies of our ancestors. Without the tattoos, many of us try to pass as Han Chinese. Unable to recognize us, our ancestral spirits have not been able to give us their blessings or offer us comfort.

I have dedicated my life to the reconstruction of traditional Paiwan culture, to show the ancestors that we know who we are. We may not tattoo our bodies, but we can consolidate our village communities, speak our language, and follow our own way of life.

I have faced a lot of opposition. In my mind, I can hear my father, a devout Christian, cursing me when I announced that my wife and I were going to get married in a traditional wedding ceremony. But even when my father called me Satan for reconstructing the culture of our tribe, I did not waver. Never have I wavered since I made my choice. I have never complained nor regretted a thing.

For I am Paiwan! This is an unalterable fact. The beauty of Paiwan culture attracts me profoundly. In fact, it has become my faith and my identity.

There are moments of clarity in everyone's life, and for me the moment of greatest clarity came when I stood on the top of the Ta-she Mountain in Pingtung County, south-western Taiwan and looked down at the old tribal village in the valley.

In that moment, I finally realized what it means to be Paiwan! I perceived the Paiwan-ness in our traditional slate houses and in our stunning totemic carvings of the hundred pacer snake. My tears gently fell. I stood there all emotional for the longest time. It was as if I were an orphan boy finally learning his parentage.

In the tribal village where I grew up, it was once hard to find traces of traditional Paiwan culture because of the severity of Sinification.

Everything Paiwan was a distant blur for me, until I met my mentors – the Paiwan sculptors Sakuliu and Vatsuku. From them I learned many precious things. From Sakuliu I learned the practicality of a Paiwan person's wisdom, while

Vatsuku shared with me the Paiwan manual creativity.

Sakuliu and Vatsuku initiated me into Paiwan culture, but I would never have been receptive to it if it weren't for my father and my grandfather.

My father hasn't always supported my decision, but it was in observing him and his father that I first saw beauty in the traditional relationship with nature. When I was a child, nature was my classroom. Everything in the mountains was my textbook. My grandfather was the headmaster of the school, my father the teacher. It is there that I learned the wisdom of my tribe, passed down from generation to generation.

I'm still celebrating my luck in having an amazingly wise grandfather and a hunter for a father. In my father, I saw the principle of coexistence between man and animal. In my grandfather, I realized the truth of coexistence of man and nature, the truth of sharing and mutual benefit.

One day, Grandpa said, "I'm old. There are not many days left for me to see the sun rise and set. The millet in my field is now ripening for the very last time. My legs no longer have the strength to kiss the land I know so well, nor my fingers the force to pull the trigger of my hunting gun. I am old. I'm old.

"Last night I had that dream again," he said. "The ancestral spirits were calling me, asking me to go with them. I asked them to give me a bit more time and let me tell all the stories I have to tell, before my life ends. In these eighty years I've lived, I've lived enough. But before I leave, I want to pass on the glory and dignity of the past to the next generation.

"The words that I've uttered, you must record with pen and

paper." Grandpa's helpless eyes, which had borne witness to the ravages of time, and the wrinkles on his face, which was inscribed with the runes of history, obliged me to comply with his request. Before he passed away, I had to transcribe his wisdom in a book for everyone to read, hopefully to understand. The hard part was that I had to do it in my own words.

"I'm dumb," I told an editor to whom I had shown an essay. "I haven't read much, and the things I write nobody reads. I can't write essays like the other people."

"Sakinu, why would you want to be like anyone else?" she said. "Everything in you is literature, things other people don't have and can't imitate. Sakinu, let everyone know all the things you keep hidden, let your life story, and Paiwan history, come flowing out of your pen." That was a revelation. I thought it over. I should be proud because I'm indigenous – I'm Paiwan! Now I am proud to tell everyone my only faith is Paiwan, from beginning to end, never to change.

In the past six years I've written a lot of things. My objective at the beginning was to make an account of what had happened to me, what I had realized, and what I had heard of the oral accounts of the village elders and their life histories. I wanted to tell the next generation how we once lived in this space.

I dedicate this book, such as it is, to my mentors, my father and grandfather, to the next generation, and to the beautiful woman by my side who has supported me the most, my beloved wife A-chen. A Siraya princess from Tainan County, she has chosen to make a life with me in New Fragrant Orchid, *Lalaoran* in Paiwan, between sea and sky on the southeast coast.

Which is where, if you will allow me, I will guide you in this book.

Sakinu Ahronglong

Translator's Note

"My name is Paiwan!" Sakinu proudly declares. "This is a fact that will not change!" But what does it mean to be Paiwan? Sakinu speaks an Austronesian language that is now called Paiwanese, but it is unclear exactly what *paiwan* itself means. It might have been a village name – it might have been the name of a plant. It has only become the name of a language in modern times. According to the "Out of Taiwan" hypothesis, Taiwan is the original homeland of the Austronesian language family, meaning that Paiwanese as it is spoken today shares a common ancestor with Polynesian languages and Indonesian, not to mention Tagalog, Malay, Hawaiian, and Maori. Austronesian is a cultural category, too, and Paiwan practices like headhunting and millet cultivation spread from Taiwan through the Austronesian sphere thousands of years ago.

In pre-modern times, Paiwanese was linguistically and

culturally unstandardized and therefore highly variable from village to village. In modern times, Japanese scholars from 1895 to 1945 and Chinese and Taiwanese scholars since 1945 have studied the Paiwan and their language. Their studies are written representations of the Paiwanese language and Paiwan culture. These written representations have, in turn, become the basis for written standards. There are now written standards for different dialects of Paiwanese, which are used in teaching materials designed to save the language. Sadly, Paiwanese is now only spoken by people of Sakinu's age – he was born in 1972 – or older. It really is a mother tongue, and it will soon be a grandmother tongue if attempts to rejuvenate it are not successful.

In supporting the compilation and use of these teaching materials, the Taiwanese government is trying to undo decades of efforts to suppress the language and the culture. Taiwan was officially Chinese until martial law was lifted in 1987, and has only belatedly embraced multiculturalism, particularly with regard to ethnic minorities like the Paiwan who were once called savages. Taiwan has recognized peoples like the Paiwan as indigenous since the mid-1990s based on a simple principle: they were living on the island of Taiwan for thousands of years before the ethnically Han Chinese settlers arrived in southwestern Taiwan in the seventeenth century, and they remain distinct. Official recognition of indigenous peoples is just one of the reasons why Taiwan is now one of the most progressive places in East Asia. Today, Taiwan is the East Asian country that has tried to do the most to make its original residents feel at home in their own homeland.

Sakinu feels at home in his village in southeastern Taiwan and is playing a role he has cast himself for. That role is to be a cultural ambassador for the Paiwan people, where "culture" can be understood in two ways, as identity and as adaptation. As an identity, Sakinu's culture is distinct practices, including the festivals his village holds and the styles of clothes he wears. To some extent, Sakinu understands these practices according to standards based on research by Japanese and Chinese scholars, but he also understands them based on his own village community experience and oral history research. As you will notice as you read, Sakinu has a very strong sense of local identity, of being a Paqaluqalu – east coast Paiwan – from Lalaoran, a village with its own distinctive practices.

As an adaptation, Sakinu's culture is an approach to survival in premodern times, when if you wanted dinner you had to hunt it or grow it yourself. Is hunting your own meat and growing your own millet still adaptive when you can now drive to the supermarket and get everything you need? Sakinu thinks so. He thinks that there's something missing in the modern or postmodern lifestyle, which has alienated many of us from nature and stranded us in screen-based media. That's why, in 2006, in his mid-thirties, a half a dozen years after publishing the Mandarin edition of the collection you hold in your hands, Sakinu founded the Hunter School. You can understand the Hunter School in terms of ethnic or eco-tourism, but if you talk to Sakinu you'd realize how sincere he is about helping young people reconnect with their original home, which remains the source of anything they could buy in the store or see on the Internet. Tragically, the Hunter School burned down in May, 2019, but then the school is a state of mind, and will, I am sure, get rebuilt.

I first met Sakinu in the summer of 2010 when a friend of mine, Professor Terry Russell, and I were doing some research on how indigenous writers write about the topic of home in their works. We wanted to interview Sakinu because in a way he doesn't do anything but write about his home. We were very grateful to him for showing us the Hunter School, introducing us to his father, who as a construction worker has visited more countries than Terry and I had combined, and for showing us his millet field and hunting ground. This visit helped me imagine the places in Sakinu's stories as I was reading and translating them. It's an honour for me to finally give Sakinu a gift in return by translating his stories.

This collection was published as *Shanzhu, Feishu, Sakinu* in Mandarin. As you can tell, the three words in the title rhyme. Sakinu rhymes with *shanzhu*, meaning "mountain boar", and *feishu* meaning "flying squirrel". As you can also tell, the English title wouldn't rhyme.

I considered calling the collection *The Sage Hunter*, the title of a 2005 feature film based on Sakinu's stories. But in the end, I went with *Hunter School*, in honour of the actual school that Sakinu built and will rebuild.

I've reordered the stories in the collection to tell the story of Sakinu's life and the lives of his fellow villagers: from an idyllic childhood to an adolescence in which Paiwan people get buffeted by socioeconomic forces beyond their control, to a maturity in which they are finally able to reorient themselves and choose their own path.

Sakinu's path is a hunter's path. As someone who as a child used to read *The Call of the Wild* by the light of the moon, I wanted to follow Sakinu down this path, only to discover that to Sakinu it's not the call of the wild, it's the call of his Paiwan ancestors. To Sakinu, there is nothing wild about a Paiwan hunter, who is every bit as civilized as you and me, if not more so. In these stories, Sakinu translates the call of his Paiwan ancestors into terms that modern Mandarin readers can understand, and I've done my best to relay-translate that call into English.

Darryl Sterk

PART ONE

A Paiwan Boyhood

The Flying Squirrel College

With the approach of spring, flying squirrels used to go in search of nubile mates, hoping to fall in love. At night you once heard flying squirrels wooing each other. Sometimes the entire valley resounded with the rhythms of squirrel courtship, when there were a half dozen flying squirrels singing the song of love on each and every tree. What a magnificent sight! What an amazing sound!

Alas, the last time I heard the flying squirrels sing their songs of squirrel love was when I was in secondary school. I didn't immediately notice when they stopped, or rather when they failed to sing one spring, perhaps because I had never fallen in love myself, either with a girl or with the mountain forest. But I knew someone who had not only fallen in love but had a lover's intimate knowledge of the object of his love.

"Hey Dad! What happened to the flying squirrels?" I asked

him one day. "Where have they all gone?"

"Sakinu, I thought you'd never ask," he replied. "It's not just the flying squirrels that have disappeared. What about the mountain eagle that used to soar over the peaks hunting for prey? I didn't need to notice the silence of the squirrels. The quiet eagle told me all I needed to know, that the animals of the forest had started to migrate further afield.

"As for why, you can blame it on the destruction of habitat due to development and on the overuse of the crossbow by unscrupulous hunters. No matter how many flying squirrels there were, hunting them night and day with advanced technology could only end in the local extinction of the species. But you can't lay all the blame on people, you know. Partly the squirrels themselves are to blame.

"The flying squirrel," he said, "is the dumbest animal in the world. A flying squirrel is so dumb it will stand there waiting for you to catch it. Maybe dumb isn't the right word. Maybe I should say stupidly curious. At night the flying squirrel finds nothing more fascinating than a bright object. All you do is shine your flashlight at one, and it will stand there transfixed, not moving an inch.

"Flying squirrels hide in their dens in the daytime. A flying squirrel may have dens in two or three trees, but it usually chooses one to make its bed in. Unless a human comes or its tree den is forcibly occupied by some stronger squirrel, it won't leave or move into another one."

I always looked up and tried to spot the entrances to flying squirrel dens in trees when I hunted with my father as a boy. It's all down to experience: as long as a person learns to see the world through flying squirrel eyes, Father said, he'll be able to find one.

For example, if you see a hole in a tree that looks damp, especially one that is funnel-shaped, you know there's no way you'll find a squirrel inside. Who would want to live in a place that makes your skin itch or turns into a swimming pool every time it rains?

But flying squirrels are still the stupidest. Every time Father discovered a likely hole, he covered it with a hand-woven net he'd tied to a bamboo pole. Then he knocked the tree trunk with his machete. *Knock knock.* At that, the flying squirrel inside instinctively flew towards the entrance into the trap Father had set. Trapped in the net, the flying squirrel struggled, making the net even smaller until it couldn't move. In the end, all we would see was a tightly wrapped grey-brown ball.

Flying squirrels may be thicker than bricks, but they are also the most hygienic animal. A flying squirrel is so clean almost every part of it can be eaten or otherwise used.

Even undigested food in the intestines can be squeezed out and enjoyed with millet wine. Old folks say this is the most nutritious part. In the village, I often see elderly hunters washing back bites of the undigested stuff from the guts of a flying squirrel with swigs of millet wine as they reminisce about all the battles they fought and won when they were young.

One time on a hunt for flying squirrels, my father said, "Son, flying squirrels are divided into 'lowlanders' and 'highlanders', just like people in Taiwan. The flying squirrels we normally see with ash-brown fur are lowlanders, while flying squirrels with dark-gray fur and white spots on their heads live higher up.

"In winter, when food is scarce in the mountains, we can see the highlanders below the ridgeline. The highlanders are even stupider than the lowlanders, which have had to learn how to hide from hunters and to avoid people in general, in order to reproduce and survive."

Once I followed my father to the hunting grounds around Pine Brook, a model alpine village belonging to the forest bureau, to hunt for wild bees. As we walked, suddenly I threw back my head and called, "Dad, do you think there's a flying squirrel in that there tree hole?"

Father looked up and smiled with pride. Softly, he told me, "Watch and learn!"

He tiptoed up and knocked lightly on the trunk. A flying squirrel popped its head out and looked around with a suspicious look on its face. It was trying to find out who had woken it up. Its vigilant eyes took in the surroundings.

I eased myself behind a tree, but by the time I had found myself a hiding place, the squirrel had disappeared into *its* hiding place. By then, Father had managed to find a branch with an offshoot. He took off his pants – no need to be shy! – tied the pantlegs together, and fitted the branch through the belt loops. If you haven't brought a net with you, you can make one. I was impressed.

I was also amused: there was Father in his old yellow rubber boots and shabby underpants. He looked so comical.

But he was deadly serious. He moved slowly and softly. It seemed like the whole forest was watching Father's every move. He approached the hole in the tree and covered it with the opening of his makeshift net, hit the trunk with his machete, and waited. And waited. But after the longest time, no flying squirrel had come flying out. Father asked me to hit the trunk hard with the axe. Still no response. All we could hear was the echo of the axe in the valley. Then he said, "Oh! This flying squirrel has definitely gone to school. He probably finished elementary."

No sooner had he finished speaking, the flying squirrel found another way out of the tree. It flew across a ravine, settling itself in a tree on the other side. We realized we had been tricked by the thickest animal in the forest. Father climbed the tree and found that the flying squirrel was so incredibly smart it had installed a back door, an escape route in the event of attack.

Father shook his head and said, "This squirrel didn't just graduate from elementary. I think it finished secondary school and has gone on to college. Otherwise how could it be so clever?" Father untied his trouser trap.

"Next time, I will catch it, somehow," Father vowed before blocking the back door with underbrush and hiding the branch to use when we returned.

"Dad, is there really a college for flying squirrels?"

"Yes, there sure is. They all attend their classes at night." I didn't get it, so Father went on to explain, "They go to night school because they're nocturnal. They often get together for midnight cram sessions on the principles of survival. Fleeing and hiding from eagles are compulsory credits. Outwitting hunters is an advanced elective."

The next time Father asked if I wanted to go hunting with him, I immediately agreed. Of course I wanted to go! Father had prepared the hunting implements. This time we were ready for that sneaky flying squirrel. This time we'd get him.

We walked a long time, so long that it was after noon before we returned to where we'd faced off with the squirrel who had lived to fight another day. We moved slowly, stepping so softly it seemed the flying squirrel had not noticed our arrival. Father told me to keep an eye on the squirrel, tracking where it went, while he found the stick. When he did, he made the same rough and ready trouser net, stood under the tree hole, and, slowly and softly, held the opening of the net over the hole. Whereupon I walloped the trunk with the axe. But no flying squirrel came flying out.

"Dad, hasn't the flying squirrel come back yet?" I asked.

"It's possible!" Father told me to knock harder. Still nothing.

Father had me hold the net while he climbed up the tree with kindling and grass in hand. "If we can't scare it out, we'll smoke it out."

He crammed the cracks in the underbrush with which he had blocked the back door with the kindling and grass, lit it and blew hard to waft the heavy smoke into the hole. Soon it was coming out of the *other* hole, the front door. But still the squirrel – a true squatter – refused to budge!

Father was truly flummoxed. Then he discovered that it had already found another hiding place, even higher up, another hollow in the same tree with another opening to the outside. It was curled up inside this hollow with its nose poking out, so that it wouldn't inhale any of the smoke from Father's fire. The only way Father knew was because he saw its nose.

The third entrance was too high up, no way Father was climbing that far. That was it! He'd had enough. He would just cut down the tree down with his saw. He sealed the first entrance – the front door – to the squirrel's den we had discovered with branches and mud. Now the squirrel was really trapped.

Father said, "This is the smartest flying squirrel I have ever hunted. I think it has not only graduated from college but also studied abroad. Otherwise, how could it know that I would come back to catch it? It's so smart to find a tree with two connected hollows and three entrances, a front door, a back door, and a side door kind of like an escape hatch."

That night, Father went to tell his father how he had finally managed to catch the flying squirrel. My grandfather said, "That flying squirrel was nearly as smart as a hunter! Lucky you caught it, or it would have shared its experience with its kind, making life all the harder for us hunters. You can imagine what humiliation it would have been for us to be outsmarted by a highlander."

Father ran a college of his own, a hunter school, where you majored in hunting philosophy. The description for one of the required courses was as follows: "Treat animals as you would human beings and imagine that you are an animal, so you will understand their habits and their speech."

When you can understand what the flying squirrels are saying, you can listen in on the college classes they hold at night, not just in order to get the better of them, but also in order to learn to respect them. I eventually figured out that Father was just joking when he said the flying squirrel was the stupidest animal in the forest. I realized he went to the forest in all humility, for it was there that he himself had been schooled in the principles of survival.

I'm so grateful Father took me hunting when I was just a boy, and I'll never forget the way he respected the creatures of nature. I've never seen the flying squirrel college, but I believe that the squirrels must go to a school very much like the one my father ran for me and like the one that I have been running for others – a place to learn the hunter's philosophy, an attitude of respect for everything in the realm of nature.

The Mountain Boar School

I could talk your ears off telling stories about hunting with my father. But if I had to sum up his hunting philosophy, which he was trying to teach me by taking me hunting, I would put it like this: relate to each creature in nature like it is a fellow person.

Maybe because I was naughty and found it hard to sit still when I was young, adults were sometimes not that happy to see me coming around, and I was the first kid they thought of if something went wrong. If someone's house got broken into or something went missing, my father would hear about it, and I would get a licking. It did not matter whether I had done it or not – all that mattered was that it was the sort of thing people thought I might do.

Father was afraid of me getting in trouble and giving his fellow villagers even more to complain about, so on weekends and holidays he would never leave me to my own devices. He would take me to the hunting ground, not just to teach me to hunt. I didn't like weekends and holidays. When I was in elementary school, the days I liked the best were Monday to Friday. On those days I could cut class, run off and steal corn cobs or sweet potatoes, make a fire, and roast 'em. Later in the afternoon, when my classmates got let out, I would slip into the line and make my way home with everyone else. Friday night, when my classmates were celebrating, I started to worry, because I knew it was only a matter of time before Father would call me over and say, "Tomorrow we're going up to check the traps."

We would walk practically the entire day before reaching my father's trap line. Sometimes the journey seemed endless, but at other times I would forget the passage of time and simply observe the things around me in the alpine forest. I spent so much time walking through the forest, even I started to notice things. I became extremely sensitive, and if anything happened, I would react immediately. Every breath of nature, every pulse, I could somehow sense.

"Poor me!" I used to think whenever my father took me hunting because of all the walking I would have to do, because I couldn't go out and play with my pals. But in retrospect, I think I got more out of my childhood than any of my classmates. My life was fuller and richer. Without all the weekend hunting expeditions, I might never have learned to relate to nature the way most kids relate to other people. I might never have realized that natural creatures have their own life histories, just like people do. For all of this, I have my father to thank. He gave me a precious gift.

When I was a kid, I had the nickname *likucu*, which in my dialect of Paiwanese means "talking all the time", asking too many questions, or never shuts his trap, so to speak.

Every time I went hunting with my father, I would often ask, "But why?" about things I did not know, had not seen before, had not heard about before, or was otherwise unfamiliar with. "What's that?" I would ask. "What's it doing?"

Father would often lose his patience and yell, "*Maya su likucu!*" *Don't you talk so much*!

Even so, I would ask him until he gave me an answer that I could understand. My curiosity drove me to get to the bottom of things. That meant that from a young age, I came to know nature like the back of my hand.

A bee had only to fly past me and I could find the hive. But the experience of getting stung by who knows how many honeybees taught me to observe them carefully and respectfully. The same goes for mountain boars.

"You know, my son," my father asked me one time, "why the wild boar gets caught in the hunter's trap?"

I thought it over and replied, "Is it that he's boneheaded, or is it that he has eyes but does not see?"

"No, silly," he replied. "It must be because he was always cutting class and missed school the day the teacher explained how to prevent a hunter from getting downwind, how to see through the disguises hunters put on their hanging snares and the traps that catch an animal's leg in a steel vice."

Well, I found that very interesting, even though I heard it from my father, a fellow who had himself only graduated from elementary school. Only then did I realise that there were some things you could not learn in books, but that were required courses in the school of hunting. (And only later, after I'd learned about logic, did it occur to me that if there are some things you can't learn from books, then there are other things you can only learn from books, and that Father was trying to tell me something about my own attitude towards my formal education.)

"Dad, is there really a school for mountain boars?"

"Of course there is. Didn't you see the boar with the camera? It was taking photos of us with a telephoto lens to turn into slides to use as teaching materials. It'll assign us each a code and tell its pupils about us. 'This is the most dangerous hunter,' it'll say, 'watch out for him, and that smaller one is pretty dangerous, too.' Sometimes it takes its students on a field trip and gets them to observe us and smell us from far away, so the next time they smell us they will know well enough to hide."

One time I was looking down from the top of a cliff with my father when we saw a group of wild pigs. "The big one is the principal," said my father, "and the one behind it is the teacher."

"What are they doing?" I asked.

"I bet it's wrestling practice," he replied. "Maybe they're training for a regional championship."

Another time, my father and I were chasing a wild pig that had escaped from a trap, over hill after hill, through dale after dale. Finally, we caught it on the verge of the Ta-wu Mountains, the place we call Kavulungan, which is to say at the edge of our hunting ground. The wild boar was tired. And I was scared, because this was the first time I had seen such a big boar up close.

My father unsheathed his machete and moved his thumb across the tip, which apparently told the beast that its life would come to an end at my father's slightest motion. It started to squeal and circle. Then it charged! My father yelled for me to climb a tree to get myself out of harm's way. From atop a branch, I watched my father fight it out with that boar. In the end, the big animal was exhausted. My father flashed his knife and stabbed the tip into the wild pig's pumping heart. The pig used its very last strength to make its last stand, but it wasn't enough.

My father patted the pig and said, "Before you give yourself to my clan, the meat on your body and your beefy hind legs, we will sing for you. Let us pray that the next time around you will run even faster and farther, so fast and far not even I could catch you, so that you can teach your children and grandchildren how to avoid my trap. That way, they won't get complacent, or lazy. That way, we'll keep one another on our toes, generation after generation."

Only when he had finished delivering this message did my father pull out the knife, the tip dripping with the wild boar's blood. I watched as the boar's spasms slowly came to an end and waited until it just lay there on the ground before coming down from my perch and patting the pig, just as my father had done. "It was a warrior among warriors," my father said. "If he hadn't stepped into the trap and injured his leg, I might have been no match for him in hand-to-hand combat."

"Dad," I asked, "what was that you were saying just now?"

"I told the wild boar we feel very thankful in my clan for the cycle of nature. My son, there will come a day when you are a hunter, too. Remember this: when you end the life of an animal you have hunted, please let it know how grateful you are. Let it hear you thank your ancestors for wisdom and a pair of legs that you can run with. Let it hear you thank it and its ancestors for the sustenance it will give. Only then will the animals that you catch go gladly into the great beyond. Only then will we receive the generosity of the ancestors.

"We are a family of hunters," he went on, "and we follow a moral code. If you have no respect for life, the ancestors will never give you any more prey animals. If you have no reverence for nature, if you fail to obey the laws that hunters must follow, then the animals, they will not run in your hunting ground – never again."

It has been a long time, but I still have the tusk from the boar that we caught and killed that day. I attached it to an armband that I often wear, not just as a token of my father's hunting prowess, but also as a sign of our respect for life.

The Monkey King

When I was twelve years old, Father told me the story of the local monkeys who had to defend their land from foreign invaders.

"Son, see that big monkey in the tree?" my father asked, raising his rifle and clicking on the safety. "His name is Pula. He has a dozen years on you, and his clan has led all of the tribes of monkeys on this mountain for generations. His daddy died when your grandfather was a dozen years old. I hear he died gloriously. It took five hunters to bring him down. He died protecting his people.

"After he died, other alpha monkeys from other tribes wanted to be king, but they were beaten back by this one. At about the time when I was born, there was a battle on Gadu Mountain that every elder in the village can remember. In that battle, the monkeys under Pula fought for terrain and status with two foreign tribes. They say that you could hear them skirmishing and screaming every day at sunset.

"The native monkeys were beaten back deep into the mountains, and the new monkeys occupied the peaks closest to our village."

Looking up at Pula in the tree, I was thinking that his daddy must have been revered by many monkeys just like him. I could tell why because he was something special. The other monkeys had seemed very uncomfortable and nervous from the moment we appeared. They were squealing and roaring. They were trying to intimidate us. But not him. Every move he made held my gaze. He was dignified, cool, and composed. He had the comportment of a king. He was every inch a leader.

The little monkeys were running around on Pula's body. Now he looked like a loving father. Pula raised his tail high and looked at me and Father, red of face and big of eye. That freaked me out. When I hid behind my father, Pula leaped to a higher branch, a prestigious place on which only he had the right to stand. From there, he shook the trunk and screamed, baring the sharp teeth that only he had the right to show. He screamed so loud you must have been able to hear him far, far away. It seemed as if every monkey in the tribe understood this as a signal because they made no more sound. It was so, so quiet. None of the monkeys dared make a peep – they all lowered their tails and sat on the nearest branch. They all looked up at Pula.

"What're they doing?" I asked.

And my father said, "Pula said, 'Behold, our territory contains fruit to satisfy our hunger and water to slake our thirst.

Remember ye this: we cannot eat the food that humans plant. We cannot endanger our lives because of our gluttony. Human beings will use things that make scary sounds. And they will shoot you down out of the tree without warning.'"

Father said, "Pula's father was killed by the hunting gun, shot out of the tree protecting his monkeys. The Monkey King does not want his subjects to break the rules – the rules of survival, no, the rules of coexistence that keep the peace between the monkeys and the human race."

Wooowooooooo. All of the monkeys suddenly started singing together. And they all shook the tree as hard as they were able. They shook the entire mountain valley, it seemed to me. Then I understood why father had not pulled the trigger. He respected the Monkey King the way he respected a village elder.

"Really?" I asked.

"Son, they are just the same as us Paiwan, they have their own social structure with different ranks in a hierarchy. Actually, they are just the same as human beings.

"Pula the Monkey King has three wives. In the past few days, his third wife has gone missing, so he has been kind of unhappy because he is worried. The king's first wife is called Yiku. She is the queen and has a special job to do: delegate tasks to the younger monkeys. His second wife is called Paling, and she, too, has a special task: she is responsible for taking care of all the little infants and for their education. And the third wife is called Suya, and her job is diplomacy. She is the one who maintains friendly relations with other tribes of monkeys by going on peace-keeping missions. The three wives support one another, which is the main reason for his authority: they help consolidate his rule. Behind every great man is a good woman, in this case, three!"

Early the next morning, my father called me awake and told me to get ready to go up the mountain with him. But he did not tell me why. All I knew was that we had to walk a long way. When we got to where we were going, Father said, "This is not our hunting ground, and it is not the Monkey King's territory, either. It belongs to another tribe."

"What are we doing here, Dad?"

"Last night an old hunter of our village told me that on the way home he heard a monkey screaming. I was worried that the Monkey King's wife might be caught in a hunter's trap, so I have come to have a look."

We had come to where the old hunter had heard the scream. We searched for a long time. We did not hear the sound of a monkey. Right when I was about to give up, my father called my name. "Look, Sakinu, over there."

Right there at a water source we found the Monkey King's third wife, Suya. I asked my father how he knew that the lady monkey was the wife of Pula the Monkey King. "See the scar on her left leg? On her diplomatic missions she has to go on distant journeys. One time she fell into a trap set by a hunter along the way. I happened to be in the area. At the time she did not know me yet. She assumed that I was the one who had set the trap. So when I went to release the iron from her leg, she bit me with her sharp teeth. But I released the leg all the same and put on a salve made from essence of camphor oil. You know, the Little Nurse ointment we apply to your mosquito bites to ease the pain and reduce swelling. I ripped a strip from my shirt to bandage the wound for her. When she left, she looked at me – she was about half a metre away, and she took a good long look at me. She showed me her sharp teeth again, but this time she was smiling. She swatted her tail around a couple of times before jumping into a tree and swinging off."

This time Suya had been caught in a trap for several days. She was hungry and weak. The part of her in the trap, her right hand, was badly infected, maybe even gangrenous. It was all red and swollen up, and you could see the bone. She was whimpering, which told my father: *It hurts so much!*

Father said, "I'm here, everything's going to be alright." Father patted her head several times. She was still whimpering. I was standing to the side, feeling very sorrowful. When he released her hand from the vice, she did not even move, as if she had some unspoken understanding with my father.

"Suya's hand is so bad that it might never be well again..." he said.

She was licking her injury and whimpering from time to time, as if to tell my father something. She said a lot of things that I did not understand. Father said she was very homesick.

The next day at sundown, Father took Suya back home, to the place where Pula the Monkey King often appeared. Suya screamed with excitement to find herself back where she belonged.

"The Monkey King'll be here soon." But the sun was setting, and the light was growing dim. It was time to leave, but Pula had not appeared yet.

"*Kama*," I asked, "where is he? Is Pula gone for good?"

My father did not speak, or at least he did not answer my question. "Son," he said. "We will come back tomorrow." And with that we took Suya home.

The next morning, we went to the same place we had wait-ed the night before. It was quiet in the woods. All we heard was the wind in the leaves, until there was a different swish, the sound of Pula the Monkey King swinging through the forest. *Woowoooo*! Today his distinctive voice carried with particular clarity.

My father said that the Monkey King had been able to smell her from far away. Soon he appeared in the place where we had first seen him. He was jumping up and down. He strenuously shook the tree and screamed, joy in his face.

He wanted to see his wife. They had not been together for a long time. Father released the chain he had put around her neck and watched as she limped very, very slowly and started to climb with great difficulty up the tree to the place where only Pula the Monkey King could stand. She leaned against him and said to her man, "I missed you so much." Then I saw the Monkey King climb onto her body and enjoy a pleasure he had not had in a long time. And judging from the demure expression on her face, she was enjoying the attention.

In the final scene to the happy reunion I was able to wit-ness, Pula was licking her lame right hand before they disap-peared together into the forest.

I saw the Monkey King and his monkeys and his three wives in the same place a few times after that. He got along well with all his wives, especially with Suya. But his first and second wives did not get jealous on that account.

One time I asked my father what Pula meant by some gesture or scream, but he answered otherwise. "Pula is so strong and supple! He travels like the wind, and his every motion is like a passing breeze. Son, do you know what animal has four hands and four feet?"

I thought about it for the longest time, but all I could come up with was a spider.

Father's answer made me laugh. "When a monkey is in the tree, it has four hands working at the same time. And when a monkey is on the ground, it has four feet walking at the same time."

"Dad, does that mean Suya has three hands and three legs?"

He just smiled.

Pula's babies are getting bigger every day. Someday they will inherit the mountain domain over which their father rules, and hopefully they will rule as wisely as their father did. And when I have children of my own, I am going to tell them the story of the Monkey King.

Grandpa's Millet Field

"Dad, where has Grandpa gone?"

My father pointed to that yellow patch on the hill behind our village.

"Dad, what is that?"

"It's your grandfather's millet field. You will find him there. He is taking care of his millet."

Gazing up, I was feeling a bit guilty. It'd been too long since I last came home, and last time I was home I didn't even notice the millet field on the hill. Now I'd seen it, there it was, the field that my grandfather was going to spend the rest of his life taking care of. I was feeling really down and started to cry. I couldn't help myself. That's when I realised how long it had been since I had come home and how unfamiliar with it I was getting. Suddenly I felt like a stranger in the place where I had grown up.

"How is Grandpa? Is he feeling well?"

"He's the same. He goes up the mountain to work every day, and he is just as healthy as before," Father said. "Since the millet gave birth, ever since the grains of millet formed, Grandpa has been going up the mountain every day and not coming back until the sun sets behind the mountain."

"Why?"

"Well, your grandfather is competing with the birds to see who can get up earlier. If he is too slow to the field, the birds will eat all the millet. And he cannot come home too early or the hungry late afternoon birds will get at the grain. Your grandfather says that it has been too long since we planted millet in our village. So it has been such a long time since the birds in the mountains got the chance to eat quality millet. They know that your grandfather planted the millet, so they told their friends to come help eat it.

"A couple of days ago some new birds flew to the field. Grandpa was so happy, like he had seen an old friend. He said he hasn't seen that kind of bird since he was young. He even lets such birds linger in the field and play. He only shoos them away after they eat their fill. He was sad on this particular occasion and even started crying in the middle of his millet field because the new birds reminded him of his childhood playmates. And now all his chums have left him. He said these birds are the spirits of his friends. He let them stay because they were all old friends. If you want to go to see him, you can take my motorcycle."

So I hopped on the old Wild Wolf 125 cc, which was like a grandfather among motorcycles. Panting hard, the Wolf lurched up the industrial road. It was longest time before the

Wolf and I arrived at the field. The ragged sound of the exhaust scattered the birds that were stealing millet and playing. They flew every which way, like they were fleeing from a disaster. For a moment there, it was like the big and little birds were trying to steal part of the sky. But soon the millet field was as quiet as a sleepy little child who has just finished a meal. I realized for the first time how big and wide the field was. I dismounted and walked to my grandfather's *tapau*, a Paiwanese word for shed, a place to rest. But I did not see my grandfather.

"Grandpa!" I called out into the millet field. The heavy grains of millet weighed down on the stalks, bending them almost all the way to the ground. Sometimes a breeze would blow, and it was like the stalks of millet all understood what I was saying and were swaying in reply. When I called my grandfather's name again, they swayed another few times.

Suddenly from far away I heard his voice, speaking the "national language" – which is the name for Mandarin in Taiwan – in the distinctive twang of mountain folk. Call it "Mountain Mandarin".

"Ah'm over 'ere!" My grandfather was waving at me. He was so short he was almost drowning in the millet. He was wearing khaki clothes like he always likes to do. He was standing at the very top of the slope.

"Hey there, you're back. When did'ja roll on in?" The redness of his eyes told me how much he missed me. The old-timer, seeing me now, could lay down all of his worries about me. Like he was putting down a big mountain boar weighing hundreds of pounds that he had been carrying around for a long time.

"Grandpa, what are you doing up here all by yourself? When did you start planting millet? Why did I not know?"

"Well it's been a right while. And it's been a long time since anybody planted millet in our village. I dunno how many more chances I will have to see the millet grow. So I went to plant our family millet in our family field that the ancestors left to us. See how good I planted it, how big and tall and strong it's grown? See how many children the ancestral seed has yielded? From a long time ago, for generation after generation, we planted millet on this piece of land. The *VuVu* of the millet you see here now, all their ancestors all the way back to the beginning of time, grew ripe on this same slope years ago. We have depended on this land and on the millet that grows out of it from the past to the present. When your *kama* got married and got ready to have a family, I gave him our family millet for him to plant. Planting the millet represents the continuation of our family life and our tribal culture.

"When I was young, everyone planted millet in the mountains. Now I am old, and I spend half my days making friends with millet. From the time I planted it, I have walked the road here every day and every path in the field, many, many times. My *kama* died when I was young and I planted millet with my *ina*, my dear mother, right here. I remember the times when we worked all day and I had no time to play. I had to weed the field and watch it to ensure that the birds didn't come eat the harvest. We especially worried about the birds when the millet gave birth. It was such hard work and it was all for our mouths," by which he meant: we had to have something to fill our bellies.

Grandpa looked at the millet field a long time, apparently lost in thought. He picked up a rock and threw it into the field and did the same thing again and again into different parts of the field. The millet stalks with their heavy grains swayed here and there. Suddenly clouds of birds from different parts of the millet field were scared off. Clouds of birds carpeted a far off fruit tree. Strange, I was thinking, I had not seen any birds fly over or heard a sound. Grandpa is amazing! How did he know?

"This kinda bird is very smart. It got a pair of legs stronger than other kindsa birds. They did not fly into the millet field, they walked. When I was young, I often got yelled at by my old mom when I failed to spot them. They often come to eat the millet, and they come in big groups. They're the same colour as the millet when it is about to be harvested, kind of dull yellow. They're hard to see. If you don't pay close attention around harvest time, you will be short a lot of grains of millet. They're so hungry we call them 'hungry ghosts,'" he said, meaning gluttonous.

"I never did like getting yelled at, so I learned me how to look hard, and I became very sensitive to the hungry ghost. Kids today are all lazy, not like in the past. Not like us kids who were true Paiwan. When my family started to plant millet, I had to go up the mountain every day to take care of it. I left before the sun had risen and I had to walk. At noon I cooked some rice that I had brought. And in the afternoon I had to wait until the sun had set before I could come home.

"Tending the millet used to be kids' work. Going on harvest time, they used to take bamboo poles with iron cans and strips of fabric tied to them and go into the millet field and wave them around. To scare away the birds. You had to go wherever the birds flew to with your pole, to keep them flying, or better, keep them out. In the past birds were less afraid of people, but they were dumb, not like birds today who have all gone to school. Birds today're keener. They're afraid of traps in the millet and don't dare to fly right in. They only fly down when they sure it's safe."

"Grandpa, why do you want to plant the millet?" I asked.

Grandpa said, "I'll give you another reason. I'm planting the millet so I can return to when I was a boy. Now I'm old, but I can see the millet that I planted. I feel a sense of accomplishment. I remember the past. It makes me think of the friends I had when I was a boy, chasing away the birds and playing in the field.

"Seeing this millet field also makes me think of my *ina*. Sometimes I get tired, and when I do I rest in my *tapau*. When the wind blows, it is almost like my mother is standing in the millet field calling me. It's like she's still alive. When I think of her, I think of the time that we spent together when we were the only family either of us had. I miss her so much I start to cry."

I looked up at Grandpa's millet field. It was so big and so wide. How had Grandpa managed to tend such a big millet field himself? Grandpa seemed to guess at my question.

"Sakinu! Take this rope, and if birds come to eat my millet you give it a tug."

Grandpa whistled a couple of times and demonstrated. I heard a tinkling noise in the millet field. I stood there smiling foolishly for a long time. My grandfather is really the smartest guy. The rope was part of a net in the millet field, like a spider's web. At the end of the rope were five different kinds of drinking bottle and bamboo cut in different shapes and lengths. It was an orchestra with a percussion section and a woodwind section. There were straw men in rags. To every rope was tied strips of cloth of different colours, and when the birds arrived to steal the millet, I just had to pull the rope and bottles and sections of bamboo would launch into a cacophonous symphony. The straw men would move, and the colourful strips would start to wave around in the millet, like a person decorated with streamers doing a dance. Sometimes a breeze would blow, and the streamers would fly like the millet field was a marching band! You know, with trumpets and tubas. Only then would the birds fly off like folks from a country market when all their trading was done.

Grandpa told me that when he rested during the middle of the day, he would tie the rope around his foot. When he turned over in his sleep, the rope would pull the straw men in the millet field and the bird-be-gone orchestra. "That's how I keep the birds away when I'm resting."

I chatted with my grandfather as I observed the millet field and he wove rattan into baskets. Sometimes he reminded me, "Have any birds flown over?" And sometimes he asked me about my life in Taipei.

"Do people pick on you in the city? There's a lot of cars, you got to be careful. Taipei is too far away. Our ancestors do not dare to go to Taipei to see you. You have to work hard. When are you getting married? I'm old. I don't know when

I'm going to die, and I'm afraid I will not see your wedding day. I want to be a great-grandfather." As I pulled the rope in my hand from time to time there came a tinkling from the millet field. And then it returned to quiet. The birds on the branches had also quieted. They were listening carefully to what Grandpa was saying.

I listened to the sound of the birds throughout the millet field again, and just when I was going to pull the rope my grandfather told me not to. "Those birds have flown here to eat the blacknits in the field, not the millet."

I was dumbfounded. "Grandpa, you did not go out to see what kind of bird it is. How do you know?"

He went on weaving and said, "I know from the call what kind of bird it is."

I asked myself, *Why can't I tell what kind of bird it is?*

Then there was another call from the millet field, and I hesitated for a long time, not daring to pull the rope. I was afraid I was going to disturb the birds that had come to the field to do legitimate business. Grandpa kept weaving and started smiling. I didn't know what he was smiling at. "Sakinu! You know what? The bird who is there now is waiting for his lady friend. In a moment, she'll fly over."

I asked him how he knew.

"I just told you, I listen to the call. Just now that bird said, 'Dearest, here I am, waiting for you, please hurry.'"

The breeze from the mountains blew intermittently, nice and cool. The millet waved, and the percussion instruments banged in the middle of the field. I ran out of the *tapau*. The afternoon sun shone down. I felt reassured, like seeing my own tribesmen. Suddenly a couple of birds flew out of the field with grass in their mouths, and they were the colour of dull yellow leaves. I picked up some stones, and I was going to throw them into the field when my grandfather stopped me.

"They're taking grass home," he said, "to make a nest for their wives. Next year when I plant the millet, they will have babies."

All returned to calm again in the field, and Grandpa told me a story from when he was young.

"When I was a boy, I sat on the rock pile with the other children in the village by the millet field identifying bird calls. I was usually the best." Grandpa smiled, proud of himself. And I was thinking that no wonder Grandpa knows sitting in his little *tapau*, where all the calls are coming from, what kind of bird it is, and whether it is there to eat millet.

Often the birds would fly in when I was not paying attention or when I was talking to Grandpa. Whether they came to eat the millet in the field, Grandpa would not tell me – he would just tell me to listen to the call. But to me, all birds sounded the same. Only once, when my grandfather told me that the birds might be full already, did I pull the rope. A bunch of birds flew up.

"How come there are so many?" I called. If I were the one who had to tend such a big millet field, there would be no millet to harvest.

Grandpa motioned for me to look into the field. Right then a lot of birds flew in. "Look, look at how happy they are playing just like I used to play with my friends in the field when I was a boy." I admired my grandfather for his experience of living with nature. For the wisdom that nature had given him. He was part of nature, friends with the trees and the rocks and the flowers. He understood them. I felt deeply moved.

Slowly the sun settled towards the mountain. The birds became even busier in the millet field, like people going about their business on New Year's Eve. They were flying around like they were getting ready for a feast. I was going to pull the rope, but my grandfather told me not to. "*Maya*," he said, meaning *don't* in Paiwanese. "These birds have come from far away to eat my millet. Some of them came from across the mountains, from the cities of the western plains, Kaohsiung, even as far away as Taipei, and some of them have flown down the east coast from Hualien and even Ilan. They left in the morning so that they could eat the millet that I planted. They have waited for this moment for almost a day. They're starving. Do not make them go away. Let them eat until they are full, or they will not have the strength to fly back home. When the sun goes behind the mountains, it will get dark and the birds won't be able to see, and they won't be able to find the way home. Their family members will worry about them, wondering, 'Why hasn't Dad or elder brother come home?'"

I ran out of the cabin and looked at the flocks of birds in the millet field not paying any attention to me or Grandpa. They were just getting their fill. I shed a tear onto Grandpa's land. My grandfather was so great – a grizzled old wise man of nature.

Grandpa called me. "Look at that bird resting on the mango tree. He's going to get married. He comes every day, gathering millet for his gift to the family of the bride. His future mother-in-law wants to see lots of millet before she will let her daughter marry him, 'cause if there's too little she'll worry her daughter won't get properly taken care of."

Grandpa whistled and picked up his cane and pointed out the tree that was closest to the millet field. "That bird has just fallen in love, but his girlfriend still sees a lot of other boys. His girlfriend said, 'Whoever can bring me the most millet today, I will go with him and sleep with him in the evening.'"

I asked my grandfather how he knew, and grandfather said, "He told me."

I was astonished. *Could a bird really talk?*

Grandfather said, "The one on the longan tree, it's just like me when I was a boy. There are a lot of old folks at his house waiting for him to bring the millet home. See that bird that just flew over? He comes every day when the sun disappears behind the mountain."

All I saw was a bird stay in the field for a while, then fly off.

"Grandpa, why do they fly away so soon?"

Grandpa said, "His mistress's waiting for him at home, she wants to make love."

Again, I was dumbfounded. *How could he know?*

The story of the millet field and the birds is a story of the rules of survival in nature that the indigenous people follow. By treating nature humanely, we show our respect for nature and our reverence. Only then is nature generous. It's not just, "You gonna reap just what you sow." It's also, "To get, you gotta give."

By this time, the sun was sinking behind the silhouette of the mountain. I looked into the millet field and pulled the rope a couple of times. I was telling the birds to go home before it got too late. Percussion instruments thumped and cracked in the field on the mountain slope, and at dusk it sounded somehow solemn, almost elegiac. The straw man now seemed like a conductor. Grandpa said, "Tell all the birds to go home before the sun goes behind the mountain. Get rid of them! It will be dark soon, and the birds will get lost in the darkness. Their wives are waiting for them. They will not be able to get to sleep if their husbands don't come home." My grandfather's story about the millet field was so charming! There were so many stories about the millet field that were so evocative and powerful.

"*Ari*," he said, *let's go*. Grandpa put down the basket he had been weaving. And he picked up the hat that he had hung on the skull of an animal. What a hat hook!

I told Grandpa, "I'll give you a ride home on the motorcycle."

"*Maya*," he said. "I'd rather walk. I'm used to it. And I have a lot of friends to say goodbye to."

Curious, I asked, "Grandpa, what friends?"

"Stones, trees, flowers, and grass. If they don't see me go the usual way home, they will worry about me." At almost eighty years of age, Grandpa took the same road morning and night. All year he stood guard in a patch of land his ancestors had opened up and in which he continued to plant. He never took a rest, not even for a single day.

Another cool breeze blew down from the mountain. Had

the birds gone home now? I was wondering. The millet was waving at me, maybe in reply, as if to say, "Goodbye, goodbye."

Grandma's Millet Plot

Before I went to elementary school, I lived at my grandmother's house. At the time my impression of her was that she liked to eat betel nut and had a big behind. When she sang mountain songs, she would get so emotional.

"*VuVu*, what are you crying for?" I would ask her. *VuVu* is our Paiwanese term for a dear relative, alive or dead, old or young.

And Grandma would say, in her thick Mountain Mandarin, "I dunno why. Whenever I sing, I start to cry."

At the time, I often went by myself into the mountains to lay traps and catch squirrels and their cousins, mountain rats. When I came back, Grandma would smile, her teeth covered in the red juice of betel nut, like a witch I'd once seen on television. That scared me. What I liked most was her smoking her pipe and telling me stories. I still remember the stories she told me – they were beautiful and moving.

During the time I lived with her, I often followed her big behind. It was like the proverbial mother duck leading a baby duck. Every time somebody picked on me or I lost a fight, I would run home and hold her from behind. But I could not reach all the way around. It was so big. And just like the stories she told, it was unforgettable.

When I was young, my grandmother planted a big millet field. It was about two hours from her home to the field. I called that place the "work site". It was a place that all the villagers held in common, a place to plant things. It was very beautiful there when the sun was setting. It was cool, the breeze. When it blew at your ears, it was like somebody talking to you. I will never forget her millet field because there was a boulder in it. My grandfather said it belonged to a kind of dwarf that used to be friends with our ancestors. The dwarves had left it there. I used to climb on top of that boulder and watch the sun set, and I would enjoy the breeze. Sometimes at noon when we were going to eat lunch, I would climb up and call my grandmother to lunch. Every time we finished work, we would climb on top and rest and wait for Grandpa to come get us. As we were waiting, she would tell me stories about her millet field.

Grandma said, "If it's breezy or gusty at dusk, that means the ancestors have come to tell us to go home. My own mom used to say, 'Shoo not away the bird of dusk, for those are the avatars of our ancestors come to eat our millet.' They want to know if our millet tastes good and how much of it there is. In the evening, they will sing and dance all night long until dawn. Then they fly off somewhere where nobody knows.

Old-timers say the place they fly to is very far away and that we could never make it there, not even if we had all the time in the world, all the time from now until the sun dies. If there comes a day when those blackbirds with three white feathers fail to fly at dusk, it'll be a bad sign for the size of the millet crop."

The boulder has been there all this time, but the millet disappeared after I grew up. But I still believe that the spirits of my ancestors are waiting to take the form of a black bird with three white feathers and come eat the millet, if ever we plant it again.

One time I went to the millet field of my grandmother and saw the stone. The wind was so strong, but I seemed to hear the sound of a festival, with song and dance. I saw our deceased *VuVu* – our ancestors – each with three white feathers in his or her hair. And they said to me, "Next year when the millet gives birth, we won't bother. Why is there so little millet?"

The ancestors started to turn into birds and fly away. I chased after them until I couldn't see them anymore. Like a flying squirrel that streaked across my field of sight, the yellow millet field disappeared before my eyes.

I woke up. It was a dream. But I believe that they are coming. So let me dream the dream again. I want to let my *VuVu* know that I have not forgotten them, that we are still waiting for them.

The boulder belonging to the dwarves is still in Grandma's millet field, and Grandma has finally planted her millet. When I go home, I often see the millet singing and dancing when the sun is hanging towards the west and the breeze is blowing. When we harvest the millet, Grandma will burn the stalks so the smell reaches the noses of the ancestors to tell them, "We have planted millet again. We are waiting for you to return at dusk."

I hope that my grandmother can keep on planting millet. Because I truly believe that the black birds that fly at dusk are ancestors dancing in the millet. I still remember those childhood days with my grandmother working in the millet field and waiting at dusk, listening to wind that could speak, waiting for Grandpa to come on his motorcycle and take us home.

Wine Can Sing

Wine is a language in indigenous society, the only kind you can drink. It's a driver of indigenous society and a symbol of continuity. It enhances the sacred character of rituals. It gets people to come together, men and women. Elders in the village say that the alcohol you brew at weddings is the most fragrant and that when a man and a woman come together their union will be as long lasting as the scent of millet when it is brewing. When you drink wedding alcohol, you can re-visit the flavour of love.

With wine, the feelings between the tribespeople get better and better. Wine binds us tighter together. It even helps us recover our lost tribal histories. In recent years, I have been trying to compile an oral history of the village, and wine has been a language for me to communicate with the elders, for us to convey our emotions. If I go and visit an elderly person without anything in my hands, he will say,

"Without wine how can we sing, and how can we tell stories?"

Many times have I, listening to elders sing their drunken songs, seemed to hear the sound of the breath of nature and the past. It's so close, so familiar. I've witnessed long-forgotten sagas and the faces of the dead. In the world of the elders, I finally understood why wine used to be considered sacred, highly esteemed, worthy of respect.

Today wine is no longer considered sacred, and most indigenous people do not esteem it or respect it. They would rather forget it. The culture of millet wine that had been passed down to us for generations is no longer treasured by the tribespeople. We now prefer what has replaced millet wine: the various kinds of booze sold by the public liquor bureau. I don't know how many kinds of alcohol the bureau sells. What I do understand is that alcohol sold by the public liquor bureau has numbed the spirits and hobbled the bodies of my people and eroded our traditional culture.

Today the smell of millet brewing is further and further from us. Our culture of wine seems long gone. We've forgotten the sight of people working hard in the millet field from dawn to dusk the way they used to do. No longer do you see people drying golden millet on roofs. In the future, people may never see the sight of everybody getting together to sing, pounding the millet in the pestle to mark the beat. In the past, if a girl was going to pound the millet, all of the young men and women in the village would come join in, and as they pounded the millet they would sing love songs and choose the boy or girl that they liked. They expressed their love in their voices. To get a girl to like him, a boy would work as hard as he could no matter what the cost.

Space and time oppress us. Once so full, our indigenous worlds are now vacuums. We have been betrayed by the liquor bureau for a long time. What have we gotten in return? Alcohol poisoning. Aneurysms and strokes. Spousal strife and family break-up. I wonder why there was no alcohol poisoning in our traditional millet culture. Why were there none of these problems? I really do not understand why the public liquor bureau would want to sell so many different kinds of the alcohol that erodes our families, our bodies, and our spirits.

Why not brew the sweet millet wine in great quantities to let everyone enjoy it?

When you get drunk on millet wine, it is a clean drunkenness. You feel very brave, as alert and limber as a hunter.

You feel as wise as an elder.

You feel as cute as a child of mountain folk.

While the rest of the world hurtles forward, faster and faster, brewing millet the old-fashioned way seems painfully slow. It's really time-consuming. You have to go up the mountain and find a patch of land and get it ready. In the past, you used to have to burn the vegetation and then use the ash as fertilizer. The work of opening the land and levelling the land, not to mention tending and harvesting the crop, was a task for all of the tribespeople to help out with. After the land was ready, the next task was to choose the most beautiful millet to plant. The elderly people used to say that beautiful millet will give birth to beautiful children who are big and numerous and only then will the millet wine be sweet and fragrant.

To grow beautiful millet, you have to go up the mountain every day, rain or shine, no matter the weather. You have to go first thing in the morning, and you can't come home until the sun disappears behind the mountain. You can't rest during the day for fear that greedy little birds will steal the baby millet away. When the millet is all grown up, you have to be especially careful. When there are weeds, you have to bend your waist and pick them until they are gone. It's exhausting work, as you can imagine. But in my memory, the millet harvest was always a raucous affair. All of the villagers would come and help. Young men and women would get together to join in the harvest. Women harvested it, and men carried it. And the little children were the gleaners who picked up the little grains of millet that fell by the wayside. The elders were responsible for bagging the millet and tying it up and for cooking the meals.

When I was a boy, I used to help out with my friends. We would often go and listen in as the older boys and girls talked about matters of the heart. When they discovered we were eavesdropping in the millet field, they would throw pebbles at us, like my grandpa did at the little birds. Some kids did not dare to make a sound even when they were pelted with pebbles. In retrospect, it's pretty funny.

After the millet was dried in the sun for a couple of days, it was stored in the granary. Whenever there was a festival in the village or a funeral or wedding, we would make the millet into wine. There is a complicated procedure to follow. You have to steam the millet for the right length of time and get the water temperature just right. The wrong amount of yeast and the least impropriety of any procedure will detract from the quality. Once everything is ready, you take a piece of clean fabric and cover it. Then, you put the brewing vat in some cool, dark place. Three to five days later, the smell of the millet is the most fragrant and the flavour the best to drink. If you miss a single thing in the complicated procedure, the taste will be off.

In the past when you were making millet wine, you had to ask the medicine woman to come and work her magic to ensure that it tasted good and to stop any malevolent spirits from making mischief in the wine. Only then would the millet wine be clean. But now, nobody understands how good millet wine is to drink or how difficult it was to make it in the past. How much sweat and toil is concentrated in a single cup of millet wine! The smell of the brew is wisdom and history, a crystallization of culture. Today, nobody practices the culture of millet wine anymore. The day the public liquor bureau came, people started to forget the taste of millet wine. They replaced wine with other kinds of alcohol, and soon their taste buds were numbed. Nobody wanted to take the trouble to brew their own wine anymore. Instead, we gave all the money we had made by the sweat of our brow to the public liquor bureau.

The environment is changing faster and faster, so fast that people cannot adapt. Left behind, they suffer all manner of injustice and oppression. Traditional social structure has disintegrated, and the hunters in the village are no longer preternaturally sensitive the way they once were. They can no longer hear where an animal is calling from or tell which animal made a line of prints. The warriors have fallen. The hunting knives and machetes that once adorned our waists are dull. They have lost their dignity. The chiefs and elders in the village have been tempted by alcohol for a long time, and they have sold their land and sold their hunting ground, leaving us less and less living space. In this way, as the price of temptation, and as the final collapse of corroded will, a big piece of land, or an entire mountain, is drunkenly given away with a stamp of the name chop. The *pailang* – the Taiwanese term for bad guy which sounds like "white whale" in Mandarin – evict the spirits of the land. Their crafty faces and self-satisfied expressions are like seeds planted in the land that was left to us by our ancestors. These *pailang* use booze to get what they want, and we indigenous people lose our culture to them. We can't beat them at their game because we don't know the rules. They are familiar with much that we don't understand. We are the ultimate losers. We don't have anything left.

But in the village, the old folks remember. "Look, see the side of the mountain over there, that piece of land was opened up by my father and left to me! And then a *pailang* came and told me, 'You'd make a lot more money if you planted peanuts, but I'll give you twice what you could make, twice what peanuts could pay.' That *pailang* was rotten. He made an arrangement with me to rent my land. Then he gave me wine to drink and got me to sign my name. Only when I woke up the next morning from my drunken stupor did I realize that I did not have the land anymore, that I had been lied to. There's no way to get it back now." He seemed to have more to say, but then he just sighed, as if that is all he could do to express what was in the end a crying shame.

Times have changed, there's no place to hide, no tribesperson can escape. A catastrophe has swept everything away. The tribespeople feel empty, fearful, unable to find a lodging for their souls. This opens the door to alcohol, which becomes their constant companion.

My father used to be an alcoholic. One time I asked him, "Dad why did you used to like to drink so much."

The answer I got was, "When I got drunk I could express myself. I could complain about all the injustice in the world. And getting drunk felt good. I could forget all my worries. I didn't care anymore. I could fill the hollow in my heart with booze."

But when indigenous people's drinking is no longer a wine culture, when it is no longer regulated by traditional norms, we fall apart. Booze has brought us more suffering than our ancestors could ever have imagined.

When I was young, my maternal grandfather told me, "Only people who really know how to drink deserve to be called true Paiwan." Many years have passed. Finally, I understand what he meant. He meant that wine has to be part of a culture of drinking. When it is, there is wisdom in wine, which represents the unity of individual, clan, and tribe. When it is, drinking isn't drunkenness, it isn't lying on the ground or in the gutter sleeping it off. That style of drinking is undignified, uncivilized. In the past, our culture of millet wine was beautiful. But now times have changed, and indigenous drinking culture has lost its original life, as well as its capacity to compel people to practice restraint. In fact, the indigenous culture of wine in the past represents the accumulation of culture, experience, wisdom. Alcohol is a medium for communication. How many people can understand the role that wine played in indigenous culture, how important it was? I admit that my people love to drink, but who was it that replaced our original culture of drinking? Who caused it to change?

In the past few years, the tribespeople have planted millet on their own land, and they have started to drink their own wine again. The old people say, "Our millet wine really is better than anything you can buy at the store, isn't it?" I believe that in another couple of years we will find our lost culture of millet wine, and that the appeal of the public liquor bureau will fade.

One time someone told me, "You indigenous folks drink such tasty wine, it's so pleasant to drink. If wine is art, then yours is the most artistic. The way you drink it is artistic, and there is even an art to being drunk. The most representative wine in Taiwan should be millet wine, not Taiwan beer or Quemoy sorghum liquor. These other kinds of alcohol do not represent Taiwan."

Indeed, there is millet wine in the earliest historical records we have, and before that there was an oral history of millet wine, which is indigenous history. It is an intangible language and it is the only one that you can drink.

Smoke Can Speak

My maternal grandfather and grandmother have always loved to sing. They like to drink fresh National-brand milk, Mr. Brown coffee, and millet wine. Sometimes they ask me to go to the corner store to buy them thousand-year-old eggs to go with the wine. When they are a bit drunk, they start to sing love songs, both Paiwanese songs and old Japanese songs. Sometimes they even throw in an old Taiwanese song:

> *Got taken to emergency,*
> *Whatever could my ailment be?*
> *Doc says I'm sick, what should I do?*
> *Got a bad case of missing you.*

My grandfather says, "We've been singing ever since we were young, and we feel that it's the old songs that sound the best. Sometimes I start crying halfway through because I remember my *VuVu* – my grandmother – and my father and mother. I've never forgotten the way I used to live when I was a boy, and how times changed when we were forced to leave Tjacuqu – the place that in Mandarin is called Big Bamboo – to make way for the South Link railway line. We took what we could, but it was such a tumultuous time, and we could hardly take the bones of our ancestors."

It marked the beginning of a terrible cultural loss. That was the time when we started accepting foreign culture. A lot of people forgot who they were. A lot of young people today have forgotten who they are. Their identification with their tribe is pretty weak. After moving and living together with other peoples, we no longer have a sense of village identity. We have forgotten a lot of traditional stories and the institutions of the lily flower, the traditional Paiwan symbol of beauty and virtue in women and bravery and hunting prowess in men.

But the move has not changed my grandparents' identity, their sense of tradition and culture. My grandmother is still sucking on her pipe and eating her betel nut. "If I stopped," she always says, "I'd worry that if ever our *VuVu* came back they would not recognize me."

As a boy I used to live at my maternal grandma's house and would often go with her into the field to work or up into the mountains to gather firewood. When we spent the night in the millet field, we used to cook dinner over the dying embers of the cooking fire. I would see the smoke rising from the flames, and my grandmother would say, "This way, the ancestors will be able to see where we are and come and see if we are alright."

I remember my grandmother used to cut a bit of meat to throw into the fire. She said that was to tell the ancestral spirits to come down to share the things that we were enjoying and help us enjoy a bountiful harvest and prevent us from getting sick. Smoke is a way of communicating with our ancestors. If we remember our ancestors when we make a fire at night and the smoke begins to rise, then the smoke will carry our odours to the place where the ancestors are, and the ancestors will smell us and come searching for us. If the smoke seems to slither like a hundred pacer snake, then that means they are coming. And if the smoke blows back upon you, that means they are sure that you are their relative and they miss you very much and they will prevent illnesses or malevolent spirits from approaching you.

My grandmother taught me that that smoke can speak and a lot else besides – that the wind can be colourful, that the waves that billow in the field mean that our dead ancestors are dancing in the millet, that the black birds that fly at dusk are changelings of ancestral spirits, that the stars in the sky come from the tears of your mother, and that the leaping of the deer is a sign of the approach of new life.

When I was young, I saw a newborn. The first night the baby was in the village, they would light a piece of wood on fire, get it burning good, then put it out and let it smoke around the baby's cradle. My grandfather explained that the smoke would carry the scent of the newborn to the ancestors, that the proud parents wanted to report the happy news to their dead relatives.

I am certain that the ancestors follow the paths of smoke from our fires to come watch over their children and grand-children.

Hawk Master

Raaaaach, spiiiiiiiiiir, peeeeeeeeet… When I was a boy, there were a lot of hawks circling in the sky above the village. They flew from the mountain over there to the mountain here. My little brother and I used to climb up onto the cross of the old church next door and sit there watching them perform. We were their only audience.

They often appeared in a flock. They circled above the mountain behind the village before disappearing into the valley. I often competed with my brother to see who would be the first to catch sight of them, because that decided who was going to be the "hawk master" for that day.

There were several birds in the flock that made quite an impression, and with which I got familiar. When I saw them, it was like seeing my *VuVu* smoking her long pipe.

My brother and I gave a name to every bird. The one that flew the highest was called Kuma. And the one that liked to dive was called Putji. The one that flew awkwardly but force-fully was called Yuma. The one that had the loudest cry was called Matu. Every bird had a beauty that belonged to it. And every bird had a beautiful name. The only exception was the biggest bird of all. He was the bully in the flock. He stole away the prey animals that other birds had hunted. And when he found prey animals himself, he never shared. My brother called him the Great Thief. When he flew near, fear and dis-quiet would spread throughout the flock. But I personally liked watching him spread his wings and fly most of all. He was really majestic.

Putji was the naughtiest of the birds. He often flew very high and then pretending to be dead went into a dive. But he had good coordination and never made a mistake. Of all the birds, he liked to show off the most.

Kuma could fly the highest, as high as the stars in the sky it seemed. He was an oddball, the strangest bird of all. We gave him another nickname, "Brother Ku". He was an elder in the flock.

Yuma gave me the biggest headache. He was a master flier but brought disrepute upon his name. He had a special way of flying we called "angling and dangling". Flying this way, he often seemed like he would fall out of the sky, and when he did, we broke out in a cold sweat.

Matu was my brother's idea for a name because his voice sounded like one of the old train whistles. It was a bright sound, nice to listen to. And it carried very, very far. When the birds all called together, his voice was the most distinc-tive.

Sometimes I would run up to the top of Mt. Gadu at sunset and listen to them call. When a dozen hawks at cloud level sing together, it sounded like a flute concert played in heaven. They were composers with their wings and dancers on the air. Sometimes they soared or turned, but they could go into a dive in a flash, seem certain to hit the ground, then pull up at the last moment and trace the line of the ridge before disappearing over it. They would reappear above Gadu, the tallest mountain in the village, riding the air currents. The activity we enjoyed the most was to go with Father into the mountains to hunt, not because we wanted to learn to hunt, but because we got the chance to get closer to the hawks.

Gadu is the place they flew to the most often, and according to my father, this was the place where the foxes, squirrels, and what we call "hill rats" are fattest because they can eat the sweet potatoes and other crops that we plant. No wonder the hawks like to fly here and eat their fill: the prey here are too fat to run and too stupid to hide. That is why this mountain was our favourite place to observe the birds.

"Hey, *gege*," our word for elder brother, "look at those birds, they're so cool!"

"*Didi*, in my next life I am going to come back as a hawk and fly wherever inclination takes me."

Sitting on the cross on the church or on top of Gadu, watching those birds flying in the sky, was part of our adolescence. We were so envious of their ability to soar in such a masculine way, such as it seemed to us at the time. Sometimes I would speak the language of the hawks with my little brother, and we would pretend we really had started flying, and we could compete with the birds to which we had given names in soaring, diving, and calling. Good times.

When I was young, my grandmother told me, "Those raptors are changelings of powerful magicians. Look, the hawk can fly without moving its wings, not like other birds that plunge if they don't keep flapping. They must use a special kind of magic: *pulinngaw*!" I believed her as a boy. And I adored the birds.

One day, my father told a story he'd heard from his father as a boy. "When the people in the village wanted to know if there was going to be a bountiful harvest, they went to look at the number of birds flying in the sky. If there were a lot of birds above the mountain, that meant that there was a lot of prey in the forest. If birds appeared behind the village day after day, then that meant that this year's millet harvest was going to be extremely bountiful. If they stopped in high trees and called, then old people used to say, 'Perhaps in 'couple of years there will be new life in the village.' And if birds were in decline, to the point that you could not even hear the sound of their calling, the magician would say, 'The harvest this year is not going to be good, the hunters are not going to get fat prey.' In the past, the elders would tell us kids that the birds in the sky are changelings of our *VuVu*. They can tell us what is going to happen."

In my own oral history fieldwork, I heard our female chief tell a story about the true love between hawks and hundred pacer snakes. It went like this: In the past there was a chief with a son called Izang who loved a girl called Tsukuba who belonged to the clan Galuljeduy. But the relatives of both boy and girl did not agree to the union and did everything they could to interfere. So the lovers arranged to meet at sunset in secret in the mountains. One day, their rendezvous was discovered by her father, who had followed them into the secret grove. When he discovered what they were doing, he was apoplectic, and he ordered the boy away and told him he would never see her again. Unable to see her boyfriend, his daughter was heartbroken. She appeared every day under the setting sun waiting in the place where she used to meet with Izang. But he never came.

One day, he heard she was going to their secret grove every day to wait for him, and he was touched but sad. He missed her desperately but didn't know what to do.

The story of their feelings for one another touched the heart of the god in heaven, too. He appeared to the boy in a dream and said, "I know how much you love her. I will help you. Tomorrow at sunset she will go to the secret grove and wait for you." Suddenly in the dream, there appeared a large hawk with very beautiful feathers, and it was calling and circling in the sky.

After he woke, he kept on thinking about the dream, not knowing if it was real or not. Going on sunset, hair started to grow on his arms, and then feathers began to appear. His toes turned into claws, and his nose grew into a pointy hook. By sunset, he was a big hawk. By then, he'd realized that the raptor in the dream was him. He beat his wings until he had the height to soar to where he used to meet her. When she appeared in the secret grove at sunset, he was circling in the sky above. When he finally saw her, he flew down and stopped on a tree.

"Tsukuba, Tsukuba!" he called and said, "Dearest, it's so nice to see you. Thanks for coming. Sorry for all your suffering. It's me, Izang, I have been missing you every day."

She was thrilled to hear his voice, but she wondered why she could not see him.

"I'm here," he said, "on the tree."

She looked up, and all she saw was a hawk perched upon a branch. It flew down onto a big rock in front of her. As she approached it, she noticed how intently it was looking at her and how familiar the expression in its eyes was. It must be him. He must be it. In her heart she called out his name, and the raptor started calling in response. But she could not understand why he would turn into a hawk. Crying, she reached out to stroke his wings and caress the head of the boy that had turned into a bird. With that, the feathers shrunk into his skin, and his wings turned into arms and his claws into fingers or toes. And his hook of a beak turned into his original nose. He was a boy again, standing in front of her. They embraced, tears of joy in their eyes, and left their worries behind.

And that's how he often went to see her, flying at sunset to meet her. Day after day, they met at sunset and were very happy. But one day, her father realised that she was not as unhappy as before and was seldom at home in the evening. And her breasts had started to stick out more and her bum as well.

Her father followed her into the secret grove and discovered them together. He grabbed her and dragged her home. "You will never see my daughter again," he told Izang. This time he made sure. He confined the poor girl to a hole, and the boy, once he had turned into a hawk, kept circling in the sky at sunset, trying to call her name, but he was unable to make the sound. He flew higher and higher and did not fly to the earth again. When the sun sunk to the west, he circled above the tree in the secret grove, but she never appeared, and he could not change back into a boy again. Not that he wanted to. Being a human being was meaningless to him now. He would be a hawk forever.

And Tsukuba was imprisoned in that hole, too weak to call out. One day, her mother went to see her and discovered that there was a hundred pacer snake in the hole but no sign of her daughter.

It is said that the stripes on a hundred pacer snake are the tracks of Tsukuba's tears when she was locked up in the hole, crying incessantly. By the time Izang decided life was no longer worth living as a man, she had curled up like a snake. It was all she could do to protest the great injustice she had suffered. Why does a hundred pacer snake hold up its head when it moves, like it is looking up at the sky? Because it is like Tsukuba, who turned into a hundred pacer snake hoping to catch sight of Izang.

In the past few years you rarely see raptors flying in the sky above the village like you used to. The village is in decline – our traditional culture is disappearing. People don't identify with traditional culture anymore, and they're moving away, like Izang in the ancient legend when he had lost any reason to continue being human. Where Izang flew to, I don't know. I do know that men from the reservation go off to make moulds for concrete foundations and walls.

One day when I was back, I borrowed my father's Wild

Wolf and went to Gadu to wait for the hawks my brother and I used to watch, to see if they would come. When the sun rose, they started calling, and they really came. There was a pair of adult birds and another pair of fledglings that were learning how to fly. I was wondering if these might be children of Kuma, Yuma, Putji, or Matu, or perhaps the Great Thief. Perhaps they were the *VuVu* of those birds, their progeny. They kept on calling and woke up all of the spirits in the valley. The sound carried a long, long way.

After a dozen years away, the hawks have come back. Every day, they circle in the sky above the village. They rise and dive. They make me remember my childhood with my brother on the church cross or on Mt. Gadu. This time, I made up new names for them. I added my last name, which means "thunder", to each of their names: Kuma Thunder, Yuma Thunder.

I don't want to lose them again, and I want to leave the story of Tsukuba and Izang to my children and grandchildren, so that the scream of the hawks will resound forever in the sky of the village and so that the people will always be able to see them flying majestically.

PART TWO

Indigenous Trajectories

Hawk Man

Sheng-hsiung was my youngest aunt's son. I remember he used to get a headache when he opened a book and had a stutter when he spoke. It was tiring to listen to him, hard to understand what he was trying to say.

At the end of the summer before high school, the school told him to come attend class, but he didn't make it more than a week, and he never went to school again. "I'm through with school," he told me, "I want to help my family make money. I know I'm not cut out for book learning."

"Well, if you don't want to go to school, what kind of work do you want to do?"

"Maybe I will help my father up on the mountain and see what kind of work I'm good at."

So he rode the Wild Wolf or drove the truck up the mountain every morning. He got up early and came home late, and he did tiring work without complaint. With him to share the load, his father could get a lot of other things done. He went out working on construction sites, too. Anytime there was a construction boom, he would take his plumb-bob and his hammer and saw and go and work in the formwork team, making moulds and pouring concrete.

One day I asked him, "Are you going to do this your whole life?"

He told me he was happy. Maybe this was his life. When God created humanity, he gave each person a different way of living and a different space for thinking. Sheng-hsiung is the guy that God made that never complained about how difficult the work was, the guy who worked really hard. He brought the money he made home to help out around the house, and he paid tuition for his brother and bought his mother a scooter. He bought himself a brand new 150 cc motorcycle, and it was a sight to see, very stylish.

Because he was gregarious and generous, or *ashali*, a word we borrowed from Japanese which the Japanese borrowed from the English "assertive", he hung out with his former classmates and friends from different walks of life. He dealt with all kinds of people. Every time I came home on vacation, I'd see him with a big group of friends at the roadside food stand or the karaoke. Sometimes late at night they would get together on the beach and play guitar and sing. There would be beer bottles strewn on the ground. He was not the person I thought he was.

One day he came over to say, "You probably think I've changed. Maybe you look down on me. I'm still the same old Sheng-hsiung. You used to take me to the river bed to steal people's watermelons or the fruit in people's orchards, remember that? Whenever you had something good you would share it, and I looked up to you like an elder brother. I would do whatever you told me – no questions asked. Maybe you're the one who's changed. And I ain't no drunk, if that's what you're thinking. Sure I get crazy with the guys, but I have never lost control. I have my own principles. When a job ends and I don't have any work to do, I let myself relax, but if I have a job to do the next day there's nothing my friends can say to get me to come out."

Looking down at the ground, he asked, "Do you look down on me?"

I did not answer him aloud, but in my heart, I was thinking, *No way, you're great!*

In Sheng-hsiung, I saw a typical indigenous guy. The times keep improving and indigenous people are forced to follow. If they cannot keep up, then they fall back and are weeded out. But we never make it to the front. It's just like my cousin Sheng-hsiung said, "I am not the kind of guy that's cut out for school. No matter how hard I try to get to know them, books do not know me. All I know how to do is nail moulds for concrete and work like a coolie."

Because of his background, many factors have influenced his personal development, factors that can be summed up as contemporary indigenous problems. Are indigenous people condemned forever to be the ones who are weeded out if they can't manage to keep up? How long are we going to have to do the most menial work, the heaviest labour, because we have not gotten a good education?

We aren't dumb, but I guess we are not smart enough, and the reason is that we do not have a good educational environment. If we did, we could learn how to think. I believe that there will come a day when we will find a balance for ourselves. When that day comes, culture and education will support each other, tradition and reality will respect each other, and identity will start to grow. We'll tell ourselves, "I'm proud to be indigenous!" People who hear that will be drawn to us and will want to get to know us.

Every person has a different way of making do or adapting. My cousin Sheng-hsiung exemplifies the choice most people make. Booze was his way of keeping a balance between tradition and the pressures that his everyday reality place on him.

One day my father called me to say that Sheng-hsiung had passed away.

How was this possible? "When did it happen?"

It had happened that morning. He ran into a taxi in Taitung City. His friend had invited him out to celebrate a birthday. He got in the accident on the way home. When I rushed home that afternoon, I saw my aunt's husband looking helpless and my auntie with tears in her eyes.

"He's gone," she said. "Yesterday he told me that he was going to work the next day. He even went to bed early. Who knew that in the middle of the night his friend would call and hound him out of his bed and out of the house? For some reason he could not say no. I heard the sound of the motorcycle, and in the morning I heard what happened."

My cousin always gave his family the impression that if he had to work the next day, he would never go out drinking or riding. I had seen that myself, and so I couldn't figure out how this could happen to someone who kept his own principles. His mom thought it was because it was so late when his friend called, and he wasn't thinking straight. But my younger brother said Sheng-hsiung had been acting weird the past couple days, like there was something he couldn't shake off. He was behaving strangely.

What a nice guy, I thought, *God should let him go straight up to heaven.* Twenty years old is the prime of youth, but God wouldn't let him enjoy it. All God did was make him suffer injustice and torment. There were too many bumps in the road, and the end came much too soon.

When Sheng-hsiung was young, his father was very, very strict with him. He used to come over to my house. He would roll up his pant legs and take off his shirt, and his calves and his legs would be covered in welts from where his father had hit him with a hose. I used to rub mentholated balm on his welts to ease the pain.

"Can I stay here?" he would ask. "I'm too scared to go home." Before we went to sleep, he would tell me, "Cousin, when I grow up, I want to be a useful person. I want to make money for my family."

The next morning, he would be gone, but I knew where to go to look for him. By the stream. That was our favourite place to catch fish and roast meat. Either there or in the secret base we had built in the mango field. We called it a secret base, but it was just a house made of straw. When we didn't have anything better to do, we would go there to cook sweet potatoes or divide up the loot – fruit we had stolen from the orchard. I can see him and me setting out traps for hill rats and squirrels. At the time we were as close as brothers, and if we got in trouble together, we would share the punishment like we shared everything. If one of us got caught alone, we would never rat out the other. He would rather get a beating than confess. At night we went to the field to catch frogs or to someone's pond to steal fish. We set out bird traps, too, and in September we caught shrike. We got chased by the guy who planted watermelons in the riverbed! The images of our exploits together kept on circling in my mind – in the depths of my heart they are inscribed. I can see them clearly as if it's just yesterday. It makes it all the more difficult to accept that he is gone forever.

I looked over his new motorcycle. It was crumpled by the side of the road. I caressed the metal and traced out the skid marks on the ground. I knew this is not how he wanted to go. But heaven or God did not give him a choice.

God was never fair to my cousin. He had an accident when he was young that left his skin covered in rough scars that would never heal. He was quite the runner before the accident but not after. His career on the racetrack ended. He always hated people asking him about his scars, which looked somehow like the feathers of a hawk spread out across his skin. And he did not like other people calling him birdman or hawkman or hawkarm. That was actually the worst for him. He did not want other people to mention his scars because it would remind him of what happened.

He was supposed to have a bath before his mom and dad got home, but one day he was watching television when he heard them at the door. Afraid of the beating he would surely get, he tore off his clothes and leaped into the tub that his sister had filled without testing the water first. It was scalding hot. His parents did not arrive in time to stop him, only in time to see him screaming, his skin peeling. That was the first torment he endured at God's hands.

"Cousin," he once told me, "after I grow up I want to make enough money so I have enough extra to get rid of my scars," so people wouldn't call him names, or make fun of him, or stare at him. In his heart, he must have often asked, "Why me?"

In the corner of his house I saw the tools that he used to nail the concrete moulds. His hammer and plumb-bob and saw. I had gone with him to the city to buy them. I started crying, not out of sadness but anger towards heaven for the injustice. *He was such a good guy, why did you have to take him away like this?* I thought again of all the places we used to visit and all the things we used to get up to together. In my heart of hearts, I have never looked down on him. I've always thought he was the most amazing guy.

The Fisherman's Lament

"Boss, I miss my family – do I really have to go to sea?"

"When you get on the boat, think about all the ladies that'll be waiting for you in the next port of call. Have another drink. You'll be fine tomorrow morning, no worries in the world."

I was staying in an old-fashioned Japanese-style inn, a room with paper walls. I can't remember what it was called. All I remember is that I had come to represent my home county in a national track-and-field meet. All of the inns in Pingtung County were full of competitors. There was just this one old inn with vacancies. I'd come back early to get a good rest before the races the next day, while my teammates all went out window shopping until quite late. But there was no way I could get a decent night's sleep. I kept staring at the ceiling and listening to these guys next door drinking and talking and singing. It was many years ago, but I remember those thin walls, through which I heard voices of those with a seemingly different fate. They were like warriors about to go out to battle. Their melody was mournful, elegiac.

"Boss, how long before I can come home?"

"Soon. We'll come back when the hold's full of fish, alright? Get a good rest. I'll be waiting for you in the harbour in the afternoon."

I heard footsteps going down the stairs and a voice giving instructions to the first and second mate. Then the owner of the voice drove off into the night, and the singing started again.

I listened deep into the night before until my curiosity got the better of me. I moved a chair and stood on top to try to catch a glimpse at my neighbour. The boards did not reach all the way to the ceiling in those old inns, so when I stood on the chair, I could see into the next room. I saw a singer with longish hair, the floor around him shiny. The boss had sounded nice enough, but I wondered what kind of deal he was getting.

When I was a kid, my friend's father from the Amis tribe who lived in the lower village would often go out to sea for the longest time and then return with nothing to show for it. One time, the only thing that came back was a corpse that was frozen along with the catch. A fisherman could count himself lucky if he made it home safe and even luckier if he made any money. Sometimes fishermen would sell themselves into a period of servitude and have to buy themselves out or end up owing the company a heap of money for one reason or another. All they could do then was sell off their ancestral land in order to pay off the debt.

Why was my neighbour, who was apparently the same age as me and also Paiwan, going off to sea? It sounded pretty sketchy to me – there was just no guarantee it would be worth it. He was going somewhere without friends or family to look out for him.

When it was almost morning, right before the cocks started to crow, I got to sleep. The first thing I noticed when I woke up was that it was finally quiet next door. I walked down the hall in *geta* clogs to the common washroom and took a piss. On the way back to my room I heard somebody say, "Hey!" I saw him sitting on the stairs to the third floor holding his knees. He was looking down at me. "Friend, can I tell you how I feel? Really bad! I'm going to sea this afternoon. I've got to leave my family, my friends, and my girlfriend behind."

I was thinking, *As if I have any mind to understand you? I barely slept a wink last night, all because of you. And now you want me to hear your pain?*

"Are you Paiwan, too? Where are you from? Taimali? I am from Peony – Mudan village. Care to chat?" I hesitated, but then he said, "You look down on me, don't you?"

I couldn't very well say no.

"What are you talking about? Why would I look down on you?" I asked, sitting down in the hall. "Why're you going out to sea?"

"I have no choice. My family's broke, and the boss says if I go fishing for three years, I'll come back a rich man. The captain promised that after three years, I might have one million dollars or even two." He sounded pretty confident when he uttered that frightening number. "After the first year I might be second mate, first mate after two years, I might well be captain by the time I return. That's what the company told me, so I signed a contract. Three years."

Could it really be that good? I felt like asking. *A million dollars in three years? With that kind of money you could come back and build a concrete house. You really think you'll be able to send money back every month?* I didn't want to hear his spiel anymore but didn't want to burst his bubble.

"How'd you find this company?" was all I said.

"Two days ago, people from the company and some of their employees from our village showed up and told us that it's a good way to make money. They gave us eighty thousand Taiwanese dollars as a signing bonus. So I signed up. The company took my ID and brought me to Pingtung to fill out a bunch of forms. And they told me that tomorrow I am going to sea. I haven't told my family – I miss them a lot. Can you understand my suffering, friend?"

For three years, he would only rarely be able to get in touch with his folks. He was like a kite whose string might break at any time. Who knows whether the boat company would really do as they promised or whether it was all a lie?

I have forgotten his name. I just remember he was three months younger than me. And his birthday was on the twenty-eighth. "Do you want to write a letter to your family in Peony?" I asked. "I can help you send it."

"No, that's alright," he said. "When I come back in three years, I will be the captain."

I imagined him wearing a uniform and a captain's hat. Smoking a pipe maybe. I told him to take good care of himself and wished him well. "Hope it all works out for you, making captain in three years and all."

When I was about to get up to go, someone came along the corridor. "Second mate, sir, this guy's staying next door. He's Paiwan, too."

"Get some rest," the sailor said. "We're leaving this afternoon, there'll be a lot of things to do on board." They were talking in Paiwanese. The second mate closed the door to the bathroom. I said goodbye to my friend the future captain and went back to my room. I kept on thinking about our conversation.

From next door, I heard a question, "I wonder if my girlfriend will still be waiting for me after three years?"

"Write her a letter, tell her how you feel." Only then did he ask me why I was in Pingtung. I said I was there for a competition, track and field.

He fell silent. I closed my eyes and realized I could make out the sound of humming from next door – the same song. He kept on repeating himself. "If you do not want me, what will I do? I am nothing without you. When I am in some faraway place across the sea, where will you be?"

He was going to leave his girl to go to a place that had no name. In his song, I heard different possibilities, different voices of fate, and I wanted to help, to give him strength. But how could I help? How could I stop what was going to happen? Or was going on a boat really the best way for him to help his family?

It's been seven or eight years now, and I still cannot forget the conversation I had with that guy in the inn. If it took three years for him to make captain, who knows how high he's risen now. Maybe he made a fortune, came home, built a house, and married his girlfriend. Or maybe not.

I have been saying prayers for him. I hope he came home safe.

I remember envying classmates whose fathers went to sea. I thought it was great because when their fathers came back, they had toys and candy from foreign lands. But sometimes their fathers came back without anything at all, or they didn't come back at all.

"Where's your dad?"

"My mom says he'll be home soon."

We'd graduated from elementary and his father had not come back yet. He wasn't coming back.

The Warrior Who Crossed the Sea

My *VuVu*, my grandmother's elder sister, says she's old. Soon she will not be able to move. After eighty-four harvests of millet, her hair has gone all white, and she has lots of deep wrinkles. But she is still very healthy and sturdy. She likes to drink, but she told me she has broken off her friendship with the liquor bureau.

Every time I go home, I take a trip down to Chinlun, to take a dip in the hot spring, to watch the sunset, and to see my great-aunt. When I do, I bring rice, salad oil, soya sauce, betel nut, or a crate of cola as a sign of respect. When I leave, I give her a fat red envelope. I'm all grown up, but Great-Aunt still sees me as a child and tousles my hair. She likes to kiss me on the forehead. And she asks me, "How is Taipei?" The expression in her eyes tells me how much she misses me, as do the tears that flow from the corners of her eyes. I am her favorite nephew. It's only now that I realise how old she is getting. She is very thin and a bit humpbacked. She walks very slowly. The older she gets the more worried I am that she might leave the world before her story has been told. She might go to dance with the ancestors soon.

Her memory's as good as it has ever been. She remembers things that happened in the past as if they were yesterday. She likes to tell stories, and I like to listen so much that I don't have time to go to the bathroom, for fear of missing the best part.

She has told a lot of stories, especially stories about her father, who she never tires of talking about. It is like her father was the most respected person of her generation.

"Let me tell you, my father used to be the most amazing, the most incredible, and the bravest of all the men in the village. He was the best hunter of mountain boar. He ran just as fast as a river deer. As a young man, he'd been to the other side of the island to Takao," – by which she meant Pingtung County – "There he fought with the Paiwan people of the southwest coast, and he even cut off an enemy's head and brought it back in great glory. At that time, we Paqaluqalu, we Paiwan of the east coast, had all heard about his exploits. His name was known far and wide. Anytime the chief of our village had a problem he could not solve, he would go to look for him. His status in the village was so high he was almost like the chief. Sometimes our chief was a bit afraid of him.

"During the Japanese occupation, the Japanese people offered to take the chief of Chinlun to Japan for sightseeing. But the chief was very afraid. He did not dare to go. He thought that if he was taken to Japan, he'd have his head cut off – that's why he was scared. He was so scared that he hid in the mountains and would not come out. My father went to find him and told him, 'The chiefs in all the neighbouring villages have all agreed to go to Japan to see what it is like. Only our village has not assigned a representative. Neighbouring villages will laugh at us and call us cowards.' But the chief would not listen to my father's wise counsel and refused to go to Japan. My father told him, 'If you do not go, I will go for you.' The chief was greatly relieved. 'If you go to Japan,' he said, 'I'll get to keep my head.'

"In reply, my father said, 'If I go to Japan as your representative, I have a couple of conditions. You have to help me take care of my family. Around harvest time, you have to find someone to help them until I get back.' After the agreement had been made and all the instructions given, my father left for Japan with the chiefs from the other villages.

"A very long time passed, but they had still not come back yet. Somebody said my father might never come back because he'd been decapitated. A while after that a Japanese police officer came to our house and told my grandmother that my father would come back. Days later I saw my father riding in a palanquin. He looked glorious and was dressed very beautifully, not like when he had left for Japan. He'd gone barefoot – now he had leather shoes. Now he had beautiful clothes to wear. 'Get a load of him now,' people said. All of the people in the village heard that my father had come back. Some didn't believe it, but when they came over, there he was. My father told all of the villagers what he had seen in Japan over the past half year. The chief asked, 'How come you still have your head?'

"My father just smiled, 'All we did was go sightseeing. Japan is a very advanced and amazing village. The streets are very wide, and there are lots of people living in big houses and driving cars. And we were all going barefoot. You don't see many feet in Japan. We'd lose a battle to them, for sure. Japanese people are really something.' For many days after that, the elders in the village would come to get my father to tell stories about Japan, especially our chief, who brought alcohol over every day to chat with my father.

"My dad, he kept telling us about all the strange things he had seen in Japan, many things that he could not understand. For example, strange crates that could talk and sing. He did not know how the person inside the crate had gotten in there. He must have been a child or dwarf to be able to crawl inside. And there were huge giants walking around on white fabric. We ran around back but we did not see anybody. We were afraid that the giants would trample us to death. There were also carts that could run themselves without an ox to pull them. At the time, the tribespeople in the village did not know what all these strange things he had seen in Japan were. Actually, the strange crates were radios and televisions. The giant people on the screens were movies. And there is no need for an ox to drive an automobile."

When my great-aunt told me these things about when her father had gone to Japan, she could not help laughing. Why was her father so stupid that he did not know such basic things?

In those days, indigenous people were only half-cooked and did not know what civilization was. And when civilization started to walk into their indigenous worlds, they thought that material civilization was simply amazing. They could not understand and were very curious. I've read that in the virgin forest in Amazonia in South America there was an uncontacted indigenous people who lived a very "primitive" lifestyle. When people discovered them, they must have thought they were amazing. I mean, there are still people that use nature to pursue the most primitive lifestyle at the end of the twentieth century. The indigenous people must have felt the outside world was amazing, too. But as they learned more about the outside world, and about so-called civilization, they must have been confused and had a lot of questions. I'm sure they had problems, too. When civilisation enters the communities of the world's minority peoples, I am certain there will be as many problems as there are stars in the night-time sky.

In the past, when the indigenous people in Taiwan were in a half-cooked state, civilisation quietly lodged itself in our indigenous worlds. There were serious questions at the beginning. There were a lot of things that indigenous people could not explain. When they tried to explain something civilized, their explanations were actually pretty funny. They seem innocent, like children. But if I was living in those times, I would not be able to explain any better. I wonder if people at the time would have laughed at me.

My great-aunt kept on telling me stories about her father's trip to Japan. "On the way to Japan, chiefs and leaders from many different villages were all in the same boat. Someone proposed a debate about who the true hero amongst them was. Many people started to brag about their fighting ability. 'I'm a hero – I've decapitated an enemy,' said one.

"'No, I'm the best warrior. Not only have I hacked off an enemy head, I've hunted dozens of wild mountain boar, and even dog bears. Quite a few,' said another." (Funny, we used to call black bears *dog bears*.)

Anyway, my great-grandfather listened as everyone took turns telling of their heroic exploits until finally, he stood up and said, "You guys keep quiet. I know that you are all heroes, but the wind is so strong, and the waves are so big, and the boat is shaking so much – what happens when the boat capsizes? We won't be able to get to Japan and we won't be able to get home either."

Somebody said, "If the boat capsizes, I'm a goner, I don't know how to swim." There were chiefs on that boat that had never seen the sea before. Even though some of them knew how to swim, they were afraid because the waves were really big. After my great-grandfather finished speaking, nobody dared to brag about what a hero he was.

"Nobody knows the personality of the sea better than we Paiwan," my great-aunt said, "for the Paiwan are a people who depend on the sea to make a living. I learned how to swim in the sea, don't you know? After the boat arrived in Japan, my father was the only one who was able to walk around, because the other chiefs were sick to their stomachs. They were seasick. The deck was covered in their vomit. When the Japanese saw what had happened, they decided to appoint my father as the leader of the tour of the indigenous chiefs in Japan."

I've heard the story of her father many times, but every

time it is like new. I know that Great-Aunt had an amazing father and that she is very proud of him. Now she is old, like an ancient tree in the mountains. One day she might dry out. She could fall at any time. I told her that when the Japanese invited indigenous people to go to Japan to sightsee, they would take pictures of them. And some of those pictures were still in the archives at the national research institute in Taipei. I promised her that I would go and find a picture of her father in Japan. She said, "Sakinu, I have to live long enough to see you bring that picture back. Only then will I leave for the place of the ancestral spirits."

I never kept my promise.

For the longest time indigenous people have been research subjects for anthropologists. We've been a source of material for scholars to write articles about. Scholars have measured indigenous people's bodies and have never thought about how to give something back. All we want is for the relevant authorities to take the piles of film in the national research institute, the ones that may be historically significant or have sentimental value, and develop them so that relatives of the people in the photographs can fondly remember their ancestors. It would also be a way for indigenous children and grandchildren to remember things that happened in the past so that we can reforge links to times that we have lost.

The Hunter Who Crossed a Continent

The last hunter in the village of Lalaoran, which in my dialect of Paiwanese means "the first ray of dawn's light", has pairs of hand and feet that were given to him by the ancestors, and he has wisdom that helps him coexist with the mountain. When I was a boy, what I liked to do most of all was watch him carrying his machete. At the time I kept telling myself, *I hope someday that I can be as valiant and courageous as him!* Who is he you ask? None other: my dad.

"Your father," my grandfather once told me, "was born in the wrong generation. If he had been born in the past, he would have been an amazing hunter. All the tribespeople would have respected him." But no longer. Father's skills and abilities as a hunter no longer win him the esteem of the tribespeople. Our mountain culture has disappeared, almost. Father, with his hunter's intuition, is the last walking embodiment of our ancestral wisdom – the crystallization of generations of experience of the mountains.

Times have changed – the environment is not the same. Our village has been invaded by an alien culture, causing traditional society to fall apart. The traditional institutions have all but vanished. Traditionally, we had a moral code that taught us restraint, but now that is mostly gone. We no longer follow the way of life of our ancestors. And as foreign culture has come in, indigenous people have gone out.

From the 1950s to the 1970s, no matter which group they belonged to, indigenous people in Taiwan left their homes to go to different distant places to make a living. They left the place that their ancestors had been living in for generations. All the mountains had to offer was no longer enough to satisfy the needs of the people. At the time in the factories and on the oceangoing fishing vessels, you'd find indigenous people. You'd find indigenous people working any other kind of low-wage, low-class job. That's the kind of job that indigenous people did. From my first memory, my father was seldom at home. To support his family, he went to work as a migrant worker in Saudi Arabia. He worked a spell in Taipei after he came back to Taiwan, but in the end, he couldn't get used to life in the big city. Finally, to try to resolve the struggle in his soul, the contradiction in his body and mind from which he suffers along with every member of his generation, he came back to the place where he belonged. The place that belonged to him.

He often sighs and says, "The only place that feels alive to me is right here! Only when I can see the mountains and the animals that live there on a daily basis do I feel alive. We are mountain folk. And you know, you can take the man out of the mountains but not the mountains out of the man. Once you have made friends with the mountains, you're friends with the mountains for life. You become a hunter not just in order to feed your family but in order to better understand the mountains and the life of nature. But times have changed, and we don't want to be mountain folk anymore, or hunters." In saying this, my father specifically meant the indigenous people in Taiwan who traditionally live close to the mountains and who rely on the mountains to make a living, for not all the indigenous people lived in the mountains and not all were hunters. Some lived on the plains, and some fished by the sea.

"One day I will be old," he said, "and I will no longer be able to catch the mountain boar, or sharpen my machete. When that time comes, who in the village community will want to become a true man of the mountains?"

Now the alpine forests are getting smaller and smaller, and I don't know where all the animals have gone. The hunting grounds have been taken away by the Bureau of Forestry. We are not allowed to hunt anymore. Their rules have left my father hog-tied, so he can no longer follow his instincts.

Once we had our own rules which guided our instincts. There's a saying in Mandarin, that we indigenous people "kao shan chih shan". Kao means 'lean on' or 'live near', shan is 'mountain', and chih is 'eat'. I think you get the idea. We don't eat the mountain, but we depend on it for our food. That's how it's always been. Our ancestors tell us that survival means having respect for nature, that's our main rule for keeping the life of the tribe going. We have to treat nature with humanity, just like we would treat a friend. It's like the relationship between family members.

Now the Han Chinese people from the plains have cut down all the big trees in the mountains and they have planted cash crops. The forests where the mountain boars once ran have now turned into orchards for tangerines. And the plains where muntjacs and river deer once pranced have now become golf courses for big shots. Tea plantations today might in the past have seemed heaven on earth for ants and bees and other bugs and of course monkeys to play in. But today the land is overused, and animals do not have a forest anymore. They have lost their living room, their space of survival. Land development, also known as degradation, has led to the extinction of animals. The sound of the mudfish in the pond and the frogs in the mud has disappeared. And the blame has been put on the indigenous people. People say that hunting is stealing. People accuse us of cutting down trees to build our homes and whittle our handicrafts. People say that by passing on our cultural philosophy we are destroying the natural ecology. They accuse us of stealing natural resources that belong to the nation. When the government promotes sustainability and emphasizes ecological resources, they seem to have forgotten that in the traditions of the indigenous people there is the notion that all things have life and that we should treat them fairly and humanely. Respecting ecology has always been a part of our daily lives.

"We are mountain folk," my father says, "and from the moment we lost our own mountain forest everything changed.

In the past when we went hunting, we did it according to the changes in the seasons. We did not go hunting every day."

This is how my grandfather put it: "If you take the bow out every day, then when will the male and female animals have time to fall in love and make love and have children? Sakinu, look, from the past to the present, everywhere there are indigenous people there are green expanses. Anywhere plains people have settled there are no trees. Mountain people do not even need to plant trees because trees will naturally grow by our sides. People on the plains plant trees for all kinds of different reasons, but the trees they plant have no life. Our trees have life and power and they grow very tall and big." The things that my father and grandfather told me made me deeply aware of how closely related indigenous people are with the life of nature.

When I was young, my father often took me up the mountain to go hunting. Over mountain after mountain – that's how you get strength in your legs. At the time, I had a lot of questions about the mountains. When my father lost his patience he would say, "Quit asking so many questions, you *likucu*! Chatterbox! Just be quiet and listen. If you listen, then you will hear… People will talk to you and sing to you, and you will hear the sound of their breathing." It took me a long time to understand what my father was trying to tell me.

But I think I eventually got it, and now, from time to time, I will talk to stones or trees and sing to them. It's fun. There, up the mountain, I never feel lonely. Because in my heart, I know that I have a lot of friends to play with, who'll sing with me and dance with me. When I got tired from walking,

Father would stop, have a smoke, and let me rest.

When I was resting, he would tell me stories about nature. One thing he said really made an impression on me, it was unforgettable. "It's the same with creatures," he said, "they have to rest and sleep, like you. When they are tired, they take a nap. We cannot make a lot of noise and disturb them. We have to let the mountain's healing power take effect. That's why, when a man is sick, everything in the mountains will help him get well."

He said only mountain folk, who make the mountains their home, can truly understand what this means. This was the beauty of my father's wisdom and experience of the mountains. There is no distance between the indigenous people and the mountains, just like father and son.

That's how it used to be, but there's been a change in the environment that has led to indigenous people leaving the forests and hunting grounds they lived in for generations. The way we lived in the past – nobody asked about it or interfered with it. Nobody said, "That's not right," or, "You can't do that." In the past, no matter who came to rule over the island of Taiwan, they had no way of keeping us from enjoying things that belonged to us. My grandfather said, "When China came (by which he meant when the Kuomintang fled to Taiwan in 1949), they trapped us with their laws, they snared us with their rules saying, "You can't do this," and "You can't do that." And now we have lost the forests that belonged to us and the hunting grounds and the rivers and the places that we cultivated for generations."

He meant that we've lost our space of existence and survival. That the traditional lifestyle we lived in the past cannot continue to be passed on. It cannot continue to develop. We cannot even build traditional houses on our own land. We have never gotten the respect we deserve. Our rights and living space have never been protected.

This is what the elders in the village say: "This space belongs to us. Why don't we have the right to use it? We were here a long, long time ago. Before the laws of China had been invented, we'd been living here for many generations." We are not familiar with the rules of the game of the people of the plain. They can't use their laws to say that we indigenous people are in the wrong. They have no right to interfere with our lifestyles on the mountain. Who is it destroying ecology by farming and mining excessively, often illegally, extracting too much from the land? Who is it who is driving the animals away? The blame for the extinction of the animals has been placed on people like my father. We tribespeople bear a heavy burden of injustice!

No wonder my father has been struggling inside himself – no wonder he's a walking contradiction. Some cultural practices he will insist on passing down, and some he will oppose strenuously. No wonder, given his life history.

But I believe that the blood of the mountains has always flowed in my father's veins, as well as a certain feeling for the mountains. Now, he just does what he wants. Mountain folk today all go to the plains to make money, like my father once did, and nobody wants to go back to his ancestral place, like my father's done.

There's no contradiction in me: only I continue in the footsteps of our ancestors, searching for nature and things that belong to me and the Paiwan people. Although the nation has taken away our ancestral forests and our hunting grounds and planting plots, the nation cannot take away my feet. I can go wherever I want. And when I feel tired from walking, I sit on a rock and I drink from a mountain stream. At night, I sleep on the ground just like my ancestors did. I feel like the richest person in the world. The plainspeople from China brought the legal notion of land title. Well, my father often jokes, "It used to be that if a Paiwan person had walked through a place leaving footprints with his own two feet enough times, that place belonged to him."

My father is happy to be a mountain man, it gives him an ineffable satisfaction and pride.

Having written all this, I feel very moved by my father's commitment to the mountains. Everything in nature is his friend. I write about culture with my pen, but my father writes about culture with his feet and his machete. In this way, he is the closest to truth and to nature and to the mountains. Now he uses his machete to write his own life history. He uses his feet to follow in the footsteps of our ancestors. By following the natural rules of the mountains, he uses his hands to continue the ancestral arts.

I still like to listen to my father tell stories about the mountains and look at him, his machete at his waist. As his eldest son, I feel like it's my responsibility to write stories about the mountains and about him, and if I didn't, it would be a pity. And I would feel guilty. From him, I have heard and seen and learned a lot of traditional things. If I do not record these things, then it would be a great loss for my village of Lalaoran.

Seeking a Son

I enjoy people watching on Taipei city streets. Sometimes I wonder why everyone here is so busy. It's so different from the pace of life in Lalaoran. The people here have no scent of the earth. Nobody stops to talk to stones or look up at the hawks in the sky, because usually there aren't any hawks to see. There are lots of cars. If the air is clear, you might just be able to make out the mountains. This is Taipei.

One day I saw an old indigenous guy near the train station. He had his back to me, but I could tell he was mountain. He had a real village feel to him. I walked up and sure enough, I caught a whiff of the dirt from a millet field.

He was wearing a khaki vest and a hat distributed by some candidate for political office. He was looking up at the destinations at a bus stop, like there was nowhere on the list that he wanted to be. He asked passersby, but nobody understood what he was trying to say or knew where he wanted to go.

Helplessness was written on his face. I rushed forward and used my best Mountain Mandarin to ask him, "Where're ya headed?"

The old fellow asked me in our mother tongue, "Are you Paiwan?"

"I am."

The old fellow happily nodded and said a lot of things in Paiwan that I didn't completely understand.

When he saw the blank look on my face, he switched to Mountain Mandarin. "I'm looking for the Yungho Road. Know the way? Where do I buy the ticket?"

I realized what he meant. There was no Yungho Road, he wanted to get to Yungho, a district in Taipei. He wanted to know where to get on the bus and whether he needed to buy a ticket before getting on.

I was ashamed that the old fellow's Mandarin was better than my Paiwanese – and angry. In the villages there are a lot of old folks who work hard to learn Mandarin to communicate with their grandchildren. But studying the "national language" isn't easy for them, and their grandchildren often laugh at them. 'Grandpa, why do you talk so funny?' We should try to see the problem from their perspective. They think they're keeping up with the times by speaking the national language. And as they struggle to speak Mountain Mandarin, which is inadequate for expressing their inner worlds, we could try a little bit harder to learn our ancestral languages, to reconnect with our elders and our cultural histories, not to mention our ancestral villages.

"*VuVu*, what are you doing in Taipei?"

"I come here looking for my son. He hasn't sent me money in the longest time. I don't got no wine to drink. No money to see the doctor. The electricity and water bills ain't been paid. And I have to take care of younger *VuVu* – all my little grandchildren. We don't have money to live on. I got someone to call my son on the telephone, but the man who answered said, 'Your son left quite some time ago.' So I come to Taipei to see where he is.

"Thanks for telling me about the Yongho Road," he continued, "I should go. I want to find my son as soon as possible and go home to the mountain. It's not nice here. There are too many people, cars racing everywhere, and no air. *Arigato!*"

The more I listened, the more unhappy I felt for him. This is not a place such an old fellow should have to come to, a place without forests or hunting grounds or friendly faces.

As for his son's generation – which is my father's generation – they have been forced to go down the mountain to make a living because life in the mountains can no longer satisfy their needs. Many indigenous people have fallen into the cities, becoming urban indigenes. They do the work nobody wants to do, the roughest tasks, in the most unprotected environments. All they have to sell is their labour, which they sell so that their fathers and mothers, their wives and children can do a bit better. That was the story of the old guy's son. He'd come alone to Taipei to make money so his family could do a bit better.

The old-timer walked further and further away. I was worried about him. Would he remember where to take the bus? Would he be able to find the only breadwinner in the family?

It had started to drizzle, and I teared up thinking about the contrast between his vulnerability and his dignity. He was so strong, earnest, independent – qualities that speak to the tenacity of the indigenous people. I stood there, intending to watch him until he disappeared.

"Hey, chief! You trying to get yourself killed? You got eyes in your head, why don't you use 'em? What are you here for? You should roll back up the mountain."

The old fellow patted his behind and got up, firm as a mountain. He was mumbling something, but nobody understood. He picked up his backpack. Still looking dazed, he looked at the rider who had hit him.

And the fellow yelled at him again, "Don't you understand traffic lights? Don't you know what a crosswalk is for? You don't belong here, chief. It's your lucky day that I didn't run you over."

I was a witness to the entire encounter. I was really unhappy and angry to hear the rider say those things. In fact, I wanted to charge over and punch him in the face and rip his stinking mouth out. That was just too much. With hearts as big as mountains and soft as the water in the river, indigenous people can put up with a lot, which is why we get pushed around and why we've lost so much of our land and culture.

There were more and more bystanders. Nobody spoke up for the old guy. The rider continued his rant. "You didn't even look at the light!"

Of course he didn't look at the light! A lot of the old folks in the mountains have never been to Taipei or to any big city. In the mountains we don't have traffic lights. You go wherever you want to. Nobody will tell you what to do. The old man'd come to the city and was behaving as you would expect, pretty much like people in Taipei. As if people in Taipei wait for the light and cross at the crosswalk. But that's the definition of how you're supposed to behave, no matter where you are. I remember in elementary school, the "life and ethics" class and the "society" textbook were all about life in the city: high rises, department stores, the zoo, the amusement park. Walking across the overpasses or down through the underpasses or waiting for the light to change and crossing at the crosswalk.

That's what we aspired to when we were young. If someone had been to the zoo or the amusement park or Taipei, he'd be very proud of himself, and we would look on with envy. In retrospect, the life we read about or heard about in school was in conflict with everything we knew. Where are there high rises in the mountains? Or zoos or amusement parks. Or crossing the road at the overpass or underpass. They weren't teaching us, only the city kids.

When I was young we used to say; "The teacher said", "The textbook said", "I heard at school". And when our parents said something different, we would say, "Dad, Mom, you're wrong!"

As if whatever was written was right. As if the familiar things immediately around us held no attraction for us because they weren't written about in a book. That was an injustice. It's just not fair to teach children the same way no matter where they are, only permitting them one way of thinking, one way of living.

It's been too long. I am so thankful for everything I experienced when I was young that gave me a memory of the forest, that made me feel connected to the mountains so I could speak to stones, observe animals, and hear the elders tell stories from long ago.

Finding a Father

"Sakinu, are we there yet? I am so tired. I'm *hungry!*"

In the darkest corner of my memory, there's an old and yellowed roll of film that I worry might not even play, but when I load it in the projector and press play, it comes to life in vivid colour. It's the documentary of a trip I took with my little brother to Taipei.

It was the end of summer vacation after Grade 10, right before school started. I took my younger brother on the train to Taipei to get the tuition money from our father, who was working there.

The year before, the year I graduated from junior high, my beloved mother suffered a traffic accident one day after dropping me off at school. She spent the rest of her life in a coma in a hospital bed. The family finances were never great, but now they were terrible. My father ended up having to head north to pour concrete in order to support the family and repay Mom's medical bills.

When she passed, all the relatives came to see her off. She struggled towards the end, waiting for the angel of death. She wouldn't get to see her kids grow up, get married, or bring home grandchildren. She wouldn't grow old with her husband. And then she was gone. It was a kind of release I guess, but when I realized she was gone and wasn't coming back, I was struck by the fragility of life and our helplessness. The angel of death can come at any time and take you with him just like that, without a reason. I started thinking about why we bother living, why we're born, and why we die. I started to understand that people are just travellers through life – all our emotions are episodes. So that when we are old, we can look back on it all and have documentaries to play in our imaginations and stories to tell to our children and grandchildren.

My littlest brother, the one I took to Taipei, was in Grade 1 at the time. He hadn't figured out what had happened to our mother or that he was a motherless child. I hadn't figured out how heaven could be so harsh and unfair. Why us? Is this a test? I said many prayers, but God did not instruct me. I couldn't change what had happened. All I could do was force myself to accept it and carry on.

The medical bills, the tuition for three kids, and the living expenses – it was a lot of money, and it all fell to my father, who no longer had anyone to help him share the burden. Father's temper got worse and worse, and he often took it out on us kids, hitting us, yelling at us. Soon he realized there was no way he was going to make enough money at home, so he decided to leave again, go to Taipei, and nail moulds for concrete – the only way he knew to make ends meet.

We'd spent the whole summer vacation tending the pineapples and soursops, unlike other kids in the village who went weeding on one of the high-mountain cabbage farms up at Lishan or assembling who knows what in a factory. My father called my grandfather to tell me to come to Taipei with my brothers to get the money for our tuition, the water and power bills, and for everything else we hadn't been able to pay for in several months. Father was working there with the husbands of my second aunt and youngest aunt and some Amis guy from the lower village. They were pouring concrete for slurry walls.

The day before we left for Taipei, my father called again asking to speak to me. I went to my grandfather's to take the call. "Ch'iang?" he said, calling me by the last character of my given name in Mandarin. "Miss me? Are you doing all right? How are Chih-wei and Pai-sheng?" My kid brothers.

Hearing my father's voice, I missed him so much I started crying.

After I reported we were all fine, my father continued, "Bring your brothers with you, I want to see you. I've got your tuition money. We can go window shopping together."

"Listen carefully," he said. "I'm working in the construction site by the west station. I'll wait for you there."

"Dad, is there no phone number or address?" I asked.

"How can a construction site have an address or a phone number?" he answered, impatiently. "When you get off the train, ask where the west station is. When you find the west station, you'll find the place where I work. That's where I'll be. I have to go to work now." He reiterated the part about where I could find him but got cut short.

"Tai Ming-fu!" someone yelled in the background. "Time to go to work, hurry up."

All he could do was hang up the phone. I was in a daze. I was thinking, *Where's the west station? I've never been to Taipei. How am I supposed to know where the west station is or how to find it without an address?*

Apprehensive, I went to tell my youngest aunt that the next day my brothers and I would go north to the capital city. In those days, anyone who travelled anywhere, but especially to the capital, ended up serving as an express mail carrier. She wanted us to bring some clothes, dried bushmeat and other 'mountain products', and *cinavu* – long wiener-shaped cakes that she had made from millet – for her husband.

"Auntie, do you have an address or a phone number?"

"I don't have it for the construction site," she said and went to get an envelope for the XX Construction Company. That was a relief. If I couldn't find the site, I could at least find the company.

In the evening I discussed going to Taipei with my brothers. "I don't want to go to Taipei. I want to stay here, I've got to keep up with my workouts," said Pai-sheng, who was doing track and field training. So my youngest brother, Chih-wei, and I were the only ones that went.

The next morning, I wrote a note and left two hundred Taiwanese dollars for Pai-sheng. He'd already left for the track. When he came back, we would already be on the train.

The train went briefly south, then west along the South Link railway line which had displaced my maternal grandparents, then north. The scenery got less and less familiar, until we had no idea where we were. Over the course of the eight-hour journey, my brother kept asking me, "Are we there yet?" He would go to sleep, wake up, and say the same thing, over and over again. "Are we *theeere* yet? Why is Taipei so far away?"

I was too worried to sleep. What would it be like when we got off in Taipei? Would we be able to find him? If we couldn't find the construction site, would we even be able to find the address my aunt had given us? I'd heard people in Taipei like to trick people from the mountains. The train went past station after station. Mostly station names I was hearing for the first time. Some of them sounded kind of funny. "Hsin-chu", meaning *new bamboo*, reminded me of Big Bamboo, the village where my maternal grandfather grew up that was moved to make way for the South Link railway line.

It was after nine in the evening when we finally arrived. There were so many people milling around. I had no idea how to get out. I was wondering, *Are we really in Taipei?* I stood there with all those things in my backpack, holding a big bag in one hand and my brother's hand in the other, looking pretty foolish I imagine, and feeling anxious. Everyone seemed to know where to go, this way and that. I was envious of all those people who knew the way home.

"Sakinu! Are we there yet?"

"I think so," I replied.

"Then where's Dad?"

After quite a while, the crowd thinned out, kind of like the tide, leaving me and Chih-wei and our luggage stranded.

"Hey! Where are you two going?"

"We're trying to find our dad. Do you know where he is?" Chih-wei naively asked the ticket taker.

"I haven't seen your father, but wherever he is you have to go through these gates to find him. I have to take your tickets. I'm sure he's waiting for you at the top of the stairs, or at one of the station gates.

"Yeah," I told Chih-wei. "Dad's probably waiting upstairs."

The neon lights were flashing when we got out. A sea of bright colours suddenly flooded towards me. It was chaos, enough to cause us to stare in amazement. We looked up at the big clock. Wow, it was late! The people in the mountains would have all gone to bed by now. Don't the people here need to sleep? We walked around Taipei Station, but we didn't see any sign of Father.

Chih-wei asked, "Brother, why haven't we seen him yet?"

"Just wait, he'll be here," I told him.

"Are you sure?" He went back to sit on the luggage, wide-eyed.

There were just too many people – was that why Father could not find us? I joined him and we just sat there, not knowing what to do. We waited a long time before getting up the courage to ask a passerby, "Where's the west station?"

The answer was, "Sorry, I'm not from Taipei."

I got up the courage again. "Can you tell us where the west station is?"

"See that sign? You're at the east gate."

I took Chih-wei and the luggage and headed west, in the direction the kind person had indicated.

"A-wei, Father's probably there waiting for us right now."

"Really?"

In the end him and I ended up sitting on another pile of luggage at the other side of the station waiting for Father, but Father never came. I became more and more anxious. I felt helpless. "Dad, where *are* you?" I wanted to yell loud enough that he would hear. Maybe the company would know the exact location of Father's construction site, and Father would be there? We called the company from a pay phone, but nobody answered. So my brother and I decided to go find the address on the envelope.

We kept walking and walking, asking people along the way. Everyone was incredulous. Imagine! Trying to walk all that way. I had no idea how far it was to Chunghsiao East Road Section Five. I had a map of Taipei I could not understand. I just knew that the distance on the map seemed pretty close.

It wasn't until we asked a lady who was about my grandma's age that we found out how far it actually was, "*Aiyo*! You'd die or fall asleep before you got there. It'd take you at least till morning. You'd better take a taxi."

My little brother had started to complain that his feet hurt. "Brother, how long do we have to walk? I'm tired!"

The luggage was getting heavier and heavier.

My father had told me, "If you take the taxi in Taipei, you need to find a mainlander, a retired soldier from the nationalist army. The kind driving an older car, it'll be safer. Don't go with someone young, you'll get ripped off, or they might try to sell you."

Taxis passed one after another, but I didn't hail one. I just looked to see if the driver was young or old. One of those "transport generals" saw us waiting there and flashed his lights. When he stopped and rolled down the window, he said, "Hey there, sonny, where you going to?"

I was thinking, *This driver is not a mainlander and he has stopped the car. He must not have good intentions.* So I told him, "Nope, we're just waiting here for someone. They'll be here soon."

Now that I think about it, he must have been well-intentioned. But at the time I thought, *That was close. If we had gotten in, who knows where he would have driven us to. Maybe he would have sold us to a factory to be child labourers and we'd never see our father again.*

There were fewer and fewer people on the sidewalks. The streets weren't as clogged with cars as when we got out of the station. The streets seemed bigger now. We walked and walked, and I saw a taxi stop by the side of the road with JUNG, *glorious*, written on the roof-top sign. That meant he was a mainlander, a veteran of the war. It was a really old car. The light was on top was yellowish and flickering like it was about to go out. I walked over and saw an old-timer with greying hair counting bills and coins. He cut the ignition, like he was going to take a rest. I tapped on the window, and the driver anxiously stuffed a wad of bills in his pocket and rolled down the window. When he saw how young I was, he said, "Anything I can help you with, sonny?"

"We need to go somewhere."

He looked us up and down, guessing we were from the mountains. He asked, "Where ya going?" I got out the envelope with Father's company's address. "Oh, Chunghsiao East Road." He hesitated. "Alright, hop in."

After we got in the car, Chih-wei stuck his cheek to the window and watched the world go by. "Brother, there's no sky. How can I see the stars?"

When the driver heard that he laughed. "Kid, where are you from?"

"We're from Taitung."

"Then you must be 'mountain compatriots'. Your little brother is cute, and he talks kind of interesting. I used to be a soldier in Taitung, you know. It's real nice there. The air's good, the girls are pretty and friendly, if you know what I mean…" He laughed. "Taitung is great, I love it. It's one of the many places I've called home. It's nice to meet you today, like meeting someone from back home. When we get there, I want to take you right to the door, like I'd do for someone I grew up with. Alright?"

I remembered what my father'd said, "You have to take a taxi driven by a mainlander, the older the better, they won't cheat you." Turned out we had found just that kind of driver. Finally, I could relax. I tried to make out the numbers of the addresses passing by. We were on Chunghsiao East Road Section Five.

"Uncle, we're there, you can let us out here."

"Didn't I tell you I was going to take you right to the door?" The taxi kept driving down the alleys and lanes, trying to find the right number. Finally, we found the bronze-framed number plate of the company, XX Construction. When we confirmed the number, we got out.

I was thinking, *Jeez, what a long way from where I said I wanted to get out.* Lucky, we didn't have to walk. If we did, we might have been walking till morning. We had so much luggage. If we didn't die of exhaustion, we would have been crushed under the weight.

He said goodbye. "Kid, be careful!" Then he was gone. The car disappeared at the corner. My brother and I were standing again on an unfamiliar Taipei city street, holding our luggage, at the entrance. We saw a sign: PRESS THE BELL.

The bell sounded for a long time before we heard someone wearing flip flops come down the stairs. A young person poked his head out and asked, "Whaddya want?"

"Do you have a Tai Ming-fu working for you, a construction worker. He is our father. We are trying to find him."

The man replied to us in Taiwanese, "Nope, he don't work here."

He seemed annoyed, like he had just gotten to sleep and we'd woken him up. "There are hundreds of workers working for the company. They all live at the sites, not here."

"Then," I asked, "where are the sites? Is there an address? We want to go to the site to find our father."

The man was a bit angry now. "You're getting on my nerves, kid! We have quite a few sites in Taipei, Taichung, and Kaohsiung. It's a construction site, the building isn't even built yet, how can it have an address or a phone number? I'm not that familiar with the business. How am I supposed to know where the site is, we have new sites all the time. What do you expect me to do?"

With a clunk the gate closed. The sound of the footsteps

going up the stairs told me all our hopes were dashed.

"Sakinu, did he tell you where Dad is?"

"No, A-wei."

"Then where's Dad?" We came out of the alley and got in the taxi of another old Transport General and told him to take us right to the station. Chih-wei was so tired. He lay his head on my knee as soon as we got in the taxi. I was tired, too. Though I didn't dare doze off, my eyelids were getting heavier and heavier.

"Hey, kid, we're there."

It turned out I had dozed off. I rubbed my eyes and looked out the window and shook my brother awake.

"A-wei wake up, we're getting out."

"Dad?" he murmured, still half asleep.

We were back at the train station. We went around it a couple of times without seeing any sign of him.

"A-wei, you wait for me here, I'm going to the construction site out in front to see if Dad is there."

A-wei sat down again on the pile of luggage. "Brother, come back soon."

I walked into the site, to the south of the station, holding out hope my father might be there, but he wasn't. There was just heavy machinery slumped on the ground in the darkness. I yelled my father's name to the sky. "Dad, where are you? Tai Ming-fu! It's me, Chih-ch'iang!"

I was so scared I started crying for real. There was no echo. I was thinking, *Are we going to have to spend the night at the train station?* I worried Father had come already and not found us and went back to his construction site. Perhaps he assumed we hadn't come north to see him. Otherwise, why would he not come looking for us – why would he not be here? When I got back to the third door at the west side of the station, my little brother raced towards me. "What took you so long? Someone came over and tried to talk to me, but I didn't know him and didn't reply, I didn't say anything."

I asked my brother if he'd seen Father.

"No, where *is* he?"

Hey, that's my question, I was thinking.

"A-wei, wait here for me. I'm going to the construction site one more time to check if Dad is there."

"Brother, I want to go with you. I don't want to stay here by myself. I'm scared." Holding the luggage, he smiled endearingly and held my wrist tight. "Sakinu, will Dad be there?"

I was thinking, *How am I supposed to know?*

We got to the construction site entrance and walked around, sticking our heads in to try to catch a glimpse of someone familiar. Then someone shouted at us from inside, "######!! ######!!" He was shouting in Taiwanese – we had no idea what he was saying. Maybe something like, "It's dangerous in here, get the hell out!"

We just stood there, stunned.

"You don't understand? Who are you here to see?" the voice said, switching to Mandarin.

I didn't know whether or not to speak, or what to say. I still hadn't said anything when an old fellow came out. "Hey, chief! Whoever you're looking for ain't here, so skedaddle!"

I stood there dazed.

"Don't you understand? I told you, there ain't no chiefs working here."

I still hadn't said anything. I got the sense I wouldn't get an answer. Chih-wei and I were still standing at the gate, looking in to try to catch a glimpse of Father. The old fellow was still standing there, too.

"Natives!" he said. Then he went back inside.

"Dad, it's me, Chih-wei!"

The old guard came out again, too, and now he was mad. "You rotten little savages! What are you hollering about? I told you a million times. Whoever you're looking for, he ain't here."

But we just stood there, paralyzed. We were too tired and helpless and scared, however brave I was trying to be.

In later years, I would visit Taipei again and stand in front of the Mitsukoshi Shin Kong Life Tower that now towers over the train station, a landmark in Greater Taipei. I would stand on the overpass in front of the tower and remember what the site had looked like before the tower was built, when I came to Taipei with my brother and got called "chief", "native", and "savage".

I took my brother's hand and led him along the road, looking for a place to sleep. I thought of going to an inn but was worried we didn't have the money. We sat under a covered walkway in front of a store to rest.

"Brother, I'm so tired. Can I go to sleep?" Then he said, "I'm hungry. I want a steamed bun and a black tea, alright? Back there was a bright sign with a 'seven'. I saw the *mantou* steaming in the window. Why would the seven store be open so late? Don't they have to go to sleep? The Wushang and Achilla stores in the village both go to sleep at night."

I handed him thirty dollars in coins and told him to go buy the buns and the tea himself. When he came back, he told me, "Brother, the *mantou* at the seven store are so expensive. I think he might of cheated me. The *mantou* sold by the grandpa in the village are only eight dollars apiece and they are really big, but the ones in the seven are tiny and cost fifteen dollars."

My brother showed me the change.

"Keep it. It's your allowance."

"Can I really keep it?"

"A-wei, let's take a short rest here, then go find Dad, alright?"

He nodded and had his meal in big bites and sips. I was tired and hungry, too. I couldn't help it – I ate Auntie's *cinavu*.

"Brother, we're not going to find Dad, are we?"

"Not today, but we'll find him tomorrow."

"What if we can't find him tomorrow?"

"Then we go home."

"Brother, where are we going to sleep?" my brother kept asking.

I was losing my patience. "We'll go to the basement of the train station, alright? There are chairs down there, we can sleep on the chairs."

"And tomorrow when we get up, we'll see Dad?"

My naive brother, I was thinking. *What am I supposed to tell ya? How am I supposed to know?*

By then, Taipei seemed like a quiet child that has just

bawled its eyes out. The streets were dead now, with barely any cars or people. All we saw was flashing neon lights.

In the middle of the night the hallways in the belly of the train station seemed so long it was like we were inside the guts of a sleeping dragon. There were no people shuttling back and forth. There were just beggars and hobos who had found a place to rest their weary heads. It was a totally different place, a different world.

"A-wei," I said, "you wait here for me. I'm going up to try one last time. You have to sit here, don't move. If anyone talks to you, don't answer. Understand?"

My brother opened his eyes wide and nodded. "Don't leave me here alone too long."

He sat on the bench, his two short Paiwan legs dangling. "Brother, hurry. I'm scared," he said, causing my legs, which were already on the way up the stairs, to halt.

I looked back and nodded, "I'll be back soon. Don't go nowhere."

That's what Father had taught me when he took me hunting up the mountain. "If you don't know the way, or you get lost," he said, "just stay in one place and wait for someone to come find you. If you keep walking, you'll get tired and hungry and will be easily led astray by *akuma*. Then I might never find you again."

Wasn't that me now? I was tired and hungry. Had I been led away by an *akuma*? I went around and around the train station but still didn't see a construction site like my father said to the west of the station. I felt so alone and helpless. Standing in the west entrance, I imagined my father coming.

Time passed second by second, minute by minute. My eyelids were so heavy they almost fell shut, and for a moment I really did get bitten by the nap bug.

When I woke up, I was crouching there under the sign that said WEST 3. Father was nowhere to be seen. Back in the village, we never had to say what we were thinking, the other would understand. Were we strangers to each other now? No! I hadn't lost faith. I was certain if I went back to the train station, Father would be able to find us.

I walked down the stairs to the basement, my legs heavy. I was wondering what to say to Chih-wei. That I hadn't found Father yet? On the last stair I finally heard my brother calling "Sakinu!" and saw him sitting there, with a policeman standing in front of him looking down. Things had taken a turn for the worse.

My first thought was that my brother had done something wrong. I ran over and asked the policeman, "Officer, is there any problem?"

"What's your relation to the boy?"

"He's my brother."

"We thought he might be a victim of human trafficking who ran away. What are you doing here?"

"We're waiting for our father."

"Do you know what time it is? Don't you know, this place gets cleaned out in the evening?"

I was thinking, *If we can't rest here, then where are we supposed to go?*

As if he knew what I was thinking, the officer said, "If you don't leave now, you'll get locked up inside here, and the door won't open until the train comes in tomorrow morning."

We had nowhere to go, and it was late. So what if it didn't open until tomorrow? The policeman said his piece, then walked down the corridor and disappeared. I hung my head and squeezed my hands between my legs. "Dad, where are you?!"

"Are you crying, Sakinu? Why are you hanging your head? Don't worry, Dad'll come find us."

My useless tears fell on the back of his hand.

"Brother, you're crying!"

Time seemed to have gone to sleep, like everything else in the world besides us. There wasn't any sound, besides the hum of the air through the ventilation. Chih-wei sat on the bench swinging his legs, looking towards the end of the hallway like he had magic sight, like...

"Sakinu, look, there's Dad!"

I thought he was joking. I tapped him on the head and said, "Quit it, at a time like this!"

"Brother, if you don't believe me, look!"

I looked where he'd been looking. *Hey isn't that Dad?* Blurred by my tears, he came nearer and nearer.

Brother raced towards him, barefoot. He looked back and said, "Brother, it's really him."

I will always remember that moment when I was about to give up hope. I cannot forget.

"Sakinu, it's Dad!" he called again. Now we three were the only ones in the basement of the train station. He walked towards us, his clothes all muddy. He was wearing rainboots and, on his head, a yellow hard hat with "XX Construction" on it.

"So here you are. I've been waiting for you at the site the whole time. I was wondering if you would ever come. I thought you might have gotten lost. Or taken away by someone. I was worried about you and thought you might have ended up here, where you started. I guessed right." My brother and I couldn't care less about his muddy clothes. We hugged him tightly. All our fear was like a boat that had lost its bearings and now finally saw the beam of a lighthouse.

"Dad, why did you take so long?" Chih-wei asked. "We've been looking for you everywhere. We thought we'd never find you. Just now Sakinu was crying. Look his eyes are still red."

Father saw how exhausted we were and said, "You must be beat. Come on, let's go get some rest at the dormitory."

Father carried Chih-wei on his back, and I carried the luggage. Before I went up the stairs I looked back – now the corridor was like a theatre after the show lets out. What was the show? Father and child reunion, the last show of the night.

When we got up to the lobby, we realized Father had mobilized the husbands of our aunts and the Amis guy. They'd all come looking for me and my little brother. Our appearance put their uneasy hearts to rest.

On the way back to the construction site, the sky was getting bright out. My father woke my little brother up. "A-wei, want a bowl of noodles?"

Father, my uncles, the Amis guy from the lower village, and my little brother and I ate pig foot vermicelli at a stand by the side of the road. That was the first time I had eaten it. I never guessed a bowl of noodles could taste so good. After I finished, my uncle saw how exhausted I was and told Father to take us back to the site and let us rest.

When we got there, we saw a muddy ground, cranes, trucks, backhoes, and a dormitory – a container for us to sleep in like sardines. If you got up in the middle of the night to take a pee, you might step on someone. We slept until afternoon the next day. Father'd taken the day off.

We went to Hsimenting to see the sights. Father said he'd brought Mom there once. Now she was gone, but the sights were the same. My first impression of Hsimenting was that there were more people than at harvest festival in the village. I couldn't get used to it. Everyone else was dressed in stylish clothes, while we stuck out like a sore thumb. One look would tell you we weren't from there – we were from the mountains. My father bought me the first pair of what I considered to be stylish leather shoes. They're no longer stylish. It's been seven or eight years now, but they still look like new. I have only worn them a few times. Whenever I do, I think of that trip I made with my little brother to Taipei to find Father. The shoes may have gone out of fashion, but the memories will never fade.

It seems to me now that our story that day is every indigenous person's story. The story of a kid from the mountains going to a place filled with people who live a different pace of life, feeling afraid of the unfamiliar surroundings but having to face that fear. You can sympathize, but if you haven't experienced it for yourself, you can't understand that fear, not really. Everything that happened that time in Taipei made a huge impression on me. It was part of my indigenous adolescence, part of growing up.

Later I realized that the west station my father mentioned was West Station of the Taiwan Motor Transport Co., Ltd. The bus station. I'd misunderstood, jumped to conclusions. And I guess it was for the best that I made that leap or that unforgettable series of events wouldn't have happened, and I wouldn't have had a tale to tell about how we found our father, or how our father found us, when all hope was lost.

PART THREE

Reclaiming What Was Lost

My Encounter With Destiny

It had been six years since my *kama* came to the forgotten old village in the mountain forest. This time Father brought me and a good friend to help him bear witness.

Father described the reason for the visit to the village. "After setting out from Tjavuali," – our Paiwanese word for *Taimali* – "I walked a number of days to set out traps for muntjacs. I kept on following an animal's tracks until, deep in the mountains, I stumbled on what had been quite a large village. There were no slate deposits in the area, so where did the slate that they used in the houses come from? It's really difficult to understand. With such a large village, why didn't I ever hear about it from the older generation? The strangest thing of all was that although I'd never been to this village before, I suddenly had a sense of déjà vu.

"When I got back home," Father continued, "I had a dream. And in the dream many people in traditional costume came to tell me, 'We have been waiting for you.' People were danc-ing and singing, and many warriors were wearing bow and arrow like they were going to battle. In the dream, people kept calling my name, and the next day when I woke up, I started to remember what had happened. Only then did I re-alise what the dream was about. It was about the village that I visited. I asked your grandfather, and he said, 'Maybe you were from that village in a previous lifetime. Or maybe they were just trying to sound out an intruder into their ancestral hunting ground.' I've never forgotten my visit to the village. I've been waiting to bring you here for the past six years."

My father climbed up a tree to get a view of the surround-ings. "We're almost there," he said, "another half an hour of riding and we will be there." When I heard that I almost started crying, because when my father said half an hour, he meant three. But what could we do but follow?

My father led the way on his Wild Wolf. And I was carry-ing my friend Min-ch'üen on a rented scooter up the forest road. In places the road had subsided, and I had to get off of the scooter to push. For the most part, these old forest roads are only used by hunters now. The trees lining the road and the wild grass have started to reoccupy the road. All that is left is a thin, wavy line for the two-wheelers. We kept starting and stopping – it was torture.

My father said, "If I were the boss at the scooter rental place, and I knew that a customer was going to come up here, I would never have rented it out. But thank God we managed to get it. In the past, a day's walk might not have been long enough to get to the village, even if we weren't carrying anything. Now, with two-wheelers and the forest road, we might be there by noon."

He undid the backpack fastened to the back of the scooter, attached his scabbard to his waist, and announced we were going to walk the rest of the way.

I parked the scooter at the end of the forestry road. I was calculating: we had set out at five in the morning and here we were. It had already taken us six hours. We must be almost there. When I was a little boy, I often went with my father to hunt in the mountains, and I had heard him say we're almost there too many times. He said this to encourage me, when we still had miles to go.

My father led the way, breaking a tortuous path through the brush, through thickets of silvergrass that grew to the height of a man until, step by step, a slate stairway was revealed.

"Here it is!" he said. "It has been such a long time. I was worried we would not be able to find it, but I knew it was in the area and here it is."

When we reached the top of the stairway, I saw a village of neat rows of slate houses. *How'd they get the slate here?* I wondered, like my father had before me. I was so impressed. Such a big village! It must have been home to a powerful clan with an intricate social organisation and a chief with formidable leadership ability. Not to mention warriors as numerous as the flowers in a thicket of silvergrass. Only with many warriors could such a big village be defended.

"Mr Tai, what are you doing?" my friend Min-ch'üen asked my father, using our Chinese family name.

My father made no reply. He had taken out the pork from his lunchbox and used his machete to cut it into pieces, which he then put on some leaves he tore off a shellflower tree, which is called a moon peach tree in Chinese. He skewered the meat with bamboo and stuck the kebabs in the earth. Then, he got out the bottle of spring water we had taken from a stream and said, "I have never forgotten you, and today I have brought these things to give to you. They are inadequate, but I sincerely want to share them with you."

He poured some spring water on his palm and, with a deft motion of the wrist, splashed it around the shellflower leaves. Then he said, "Let our feelings for each other be like the 'flower of the wave,'" – our term for the spindrift that graces the undulations of the sea. "We have purified our hearts to come and see you and put all hateful things behind us. Let the water nourish us."

My father sat down and told me and my friend, "We have come to the place of the ancestors, and we have to act according to the tradition and come with sincerity in our hearts. We can only hope that they will accept us, ensure that we are comfortable and safe, and communicate with us as their intimates. I told them I have kept them in my heart, that I think of them every day, to put their hearts at ease."

My father, Min-ch'üen, and I sat there in a circle praying. I suddenly felt like there were a lot of people around us. I closed my eyes and heard my father say another prayer. It went like this: "*VuVu*, we have come to see you. I am Vasakalan, a man of Lalaoran village and our family name is Ahronglong. My great-grandfather was called Sakinu, and the two people that are sitting by me are my son, who is called Sakinu, too, and a 'white boy', my son's friend." – I guess compared to me, he was pretty white.

"I hope that you will accept us," my father continued, "and give us wisdom. Let these two young people approach you in peace. We all love everything Paiwan. Please teach us about our tradition."

When I opened my eyes, we seemed to have travelled back into the past. I saw the restrained lifestyle that people led in the village long ago. The villagers were looking back at us. It was like a lot of people were watching our every move.

"Son, be careful when you step onto the slate, you might be standing where an ancestor is sleeping."

"Father, this village seems so full of life."

"Yes, the ancestors have been sleeping and spending their afterlives here. You probably feel like someone is watching you."

Indeed, my hair was standing on end. Min-ch'üen and I walked along the slate path in the village in search of traces of the ancestors, to witness the wisdom that our Paiwan ancestors layered in their lives, like the slate they layered up to make their huts.

A lot of questions kept looping through my mind. I still don't have the answers. Such a big village – where are their progeny today? Such thick slabs of slate – where were they moved from? There was only one source of drinking water within one hundred metres of the village, and the flow was so small it was like a child peeing. How did they get enough water for the entire village to use? Maybe they embraced the hardship of the environment by pooling their strength like the men who made the pyramids. Maybe people of the past were all like Hercules and could easily move such thick slabs of slate.

My father was cleaning up the house of the chief. It was easy to see whose house it was based on the size, the construction, and the quality of slate that was used. And out in front there was a platform, also made of slate, from which the chief could address his people. And in the centre of the platform, there was an upright slab of slate that was twice as tall as me!

I unsheathed the knife at my hip and shouted. My voice passed through the cracks in the slate and resonated in the empty houses. After the longest time, the echo came like a lazy snake that had been hiding in the world of the ancestors below the earth. When I put the knife back in the scabbard, I heard a lot of voices singing and speaking, replying loud and clear. I crouched on the platform, the dais perhaps, in front of that tall slab of slate and looked up at the sky. The tall trees of the forest through which we'd come closed in around us, covering the clouds. Maybe that's the reason why the ancient village was still intact, because ordinary people, archaeologists, and anthropologists had not had a chance to destroy it. I admired the wise ancestors who'd selected such a place to raise their children, a place where their progeny would be safe.

There was a precipitous drop to the front of the village, a gully to the left – with a source of drinking water inside – and a stone wall in four sections of different heights to the right.

My father explained it was a place to lay ambushes, store guns, or lay traps to generally hamper the movements of the enemy. Finally, above the village was a broad field – a meeting ground for young people and a training ground for warriors. Any time there was an incursion into the village, the warriors could come down from the field and deal with it. From up there they had a commanding view.

My father shook his head and said, "What could have happened to such a strong Paiwan clan? I just don't get it. If their progeny were still around, we should have heard about them."

Min-ch'üen walked up to me and confided, "The moment you took out your knife, I saw warriors holding spears and arrows standing in front of the platform. I heard them shout in response to your shout, as if they were about to go off to war. And when you put your knife back in the scabbard, right in that instant, they went blurry and disappeared before my very eyes. Maybe in a previous lifetime you were a warrior of this village, a great warrior who survived a hundred battles. Maybe you were their commander."

"I was thinking the same thing. That would explain why the place seemed so familiar."

My father unbelted his scarab, took off his rubber boots to use as a pillow, and lay down on the platform to take an afternoon nap. Min-ch'üen and I were still looking around. Suddenly it got darker out, and once again I had that familiar feeling. Before my eyes another amazing scene appeared: people pounding millet and singing and children running around naked. Elderly ladies were sun-drying millet on the roofs, and venerable men were teaching the arts of carving and hunting. The chief was instructing the village youth, and the hunters were carrying a bountiful harvest home. Everyone was celebrating by singing, dancing, and drinking. It was like viewing clips from a documentary.

"Sakinu!" someone said. I looked back at Min-ch'üen, and he was pointing, but when I turned my head to look, whatever it was had disappeared. Had I just travelled through time and returned to the spiritual space of the old village? I blinked my eyes hard and wondered what had just happened.

"Did you see what I saw?" I asked.

"What? See what? I've been here the entire time. Look at this character, *ch'ing*, in relief on this broken urn."

Ch'ing means *clarity*, but this was probably referring to the Ch'ing dynasty, whose rule over Taiwan ended in 1895. At the time, Paiwan people were trading with Chinese people from the plains. This old urn was within the ruin of the chief's walls. It must have belonged to him. When I was a boy, I heard that Paiwan houses used to contain many trap doors to hide precious things. I tested parts of the wall and floor with a piece of wood. They didn't sound hollow – they sounded solid. I kept tapping for the longest time.

My father woke up and told me not to tap, lest I awaken the sleeping ancestors.

"Sakinu, come over here. What's this?"

It was another clay urn, but this one was Paiwan – you could tell by the twin hundred pacer snakes that adorned it. The slate roof had just about caved in, but this urn was intact, time had not shattered it. It was of fine workmanship – a square base with a concave body. And it was as good as the day it was made. It must be the will of heaven that a shard of slate had fallen over the mouth of the urn, keeping the rain out. That's why the urn had not cracked after more than a century of exposure to the elements.

I was thinking, *People of the chiefly clan, I would like to take this clay urn home and preserve it, if that is alright with you. Please say yes. I will take good care of it. It will no longer have to endure the wind and weather, buried on the premises of the chief's dwelling place. And I will teach my children and grandchildren about this place, so that it is never forgotten. I will tell them what happened to their father and grandfather here. I will pass on this story to the next generation.*

I wrapped it up in layer after layer of moon peach leaves and then taro. That I put in a net bag I had made with some wild rattan, to carry it home. Finally, I tied it up with a rain-coat, so that it would stay dry no matter what. This was all in order to show the ancestors that the urn would be in safe hands.

My father told me and Min-ch'üen, "We have to go now. We still have a six-hour trip ahead of us."

We returned to the place where we had first entered the village. My father put offerings on a piece of slate and said, "Here is some bread for your children to share, and here is some coffee for people that have to stay up late into the night. And here is a bottle of barley-flavoured tea, out of respect for the ritual practitioner and the medicine man. There is also a bottle of sparkling water for everybody to drink and some white rice for the chief and for warriors that have died in battle. I leave these things here and hope that you can share them, so that our friendship will last forever. We are leaving now. Thank you for guiding us and keeping us safe here today."

The warm late-afternoon sun was spilling through the leaves of the trees that protected the village. The moment we left, I heard the sound of many people talking. "When are you going to come again? Don't forget about us!"

Bringing up the rear, I looked back. I thought of their shy, attentive, curious expressions. I had seen all of the people in the village – men and women, young and old, and people in the prime of life. I had seen them all singing together in unison with the chief. I started crying and waved goodbye to them. This time I saw them clearly.

"Yes, I will miss you," I said under my breath with tears in my eyes. "I have to leave now. I don't know when I will be able to come again. I will always remember this encounter." Then I turned my back on the village and followed the footprints in the grass that my father and Min-ch'üen had left. I did not look back again. But I kept on thinking that if I had a choice, I would give up everything that I have now and return to their world to help them and live together with them.

When we came out of the big dense forest, I noticed how close we were to Kavulungan, Ta-wu Mountain. My father pointed out the eclipse of the sun as it went behind the highest peak. That is a sacred place for the Paiwan people. It was so red, the setting sun. I looked back towards the old village, but it had vanished. It seemed to be wearing a camouflage cloak. Protected by nature, the villagers dwell on their own in a forgotten neck of the woods.

On the way up the mountain I had not realised that we

had been enfolded in level after level of hills. On the way back down, I paused to take in the sublime beauty of the alpine expanses, through which currents in a sea of clouds coursed. These were the true mountains, I felt. It was so immediate and intimate. The alpine silhouette rose and fell like a woman's figure. The now sparse sunlight fell on the sacred place of my people. Then it was dark. It was so calm at night. I did not talk to Min-ch'üen, whose turn it was to drive. I just sat quietly on the back of the scooter thinking about that day's journey and thinking of how I would tell my children and grandchildren about this place, home to a friendly people.

Later, around a fire, I tried with Min-ch'üen to articulate what had happened that day, as we ate the chicken my father had roasted. Suddenly he said, "Oh no! I brought a camera to Taitung, but I forgot to bring it today."

I replied that I had reminded myself to bring mine with me from Taipei but realized I had forgotten it when I got off the plane. I had left it at home.

My father laughed and said, "That is the arrangement of the ancestors. You forgot because they were afraid that the pictures you would have taken might have brought their home to harm. They want to keep it secret. The ancestors must be hinting that if you really miss them, then you can go yourself to visit them by yourself. That's what they mean."

If my father was right, that they did not want to be disturbed, I was very happy to seal my lips, to keep their secret.

That night I had a dream, though I did not know it was a dream while I was in it, in which a crowd of villagers brought me food and drink, and someone said, "You've finally come back to us. We've finally found you, the one we have been waiting for."

The person who addressed me was an elder, who told me the history of the village. Later the chief appeared and he called my name. "Sakinu!"

Then appeared a young person whose skin was covered in tattoos. Around his arm, he wore a bracelet made of mountain boar teeth, and at his waist he had a machete. He had long hair and thick legs. He looked so familiar. He talked to me and said, "I am Sakinu, your previous incarnation and a wise man of the village. I observed you all day, every move you made. And every move you made was just like me when I was young. I saw my own air of authority in you. You are a man who will govern the youth and able-bodied men of your village and win the respect of neighbouring villages."

I kept hearing voices saying, "We have waited for you so long," and, "We knew that you would come." And we joined hands and danced as slowly as a languid hundred pacer snake – the warrior dance. And the person in front was me in my previous incarnation, fierce and vigorous, now in the flush of youth.

It was like I had seen him – myself – go from old to young, as if watching a video play in reverse. In the end, the chief said, "Thank you for the bread and tea and coffee and sparkling water that you left for us to eat and drink, the things of your world. Please keep the clay pot for us and preserve it so that your children will remember that you have visited us today."

The next day, I told my father and my grandfather about the dream. My grandfather said, "You are a person from their village. They want to see you again. That clay pot represents the connection between you and them. They will help you. If the clay pot had broken on the way home, that would have meant that they were unwilling for you to take it in the first place. Thank God the pot is still in one piece. It will grant you wisdom and power."

I still have that pot today and keep it as a family heirloom, a symbol in a story I hope continues to be told, generation after generation.

None of the Paiwan elders I talked to in my village have heard about the lost clan in the sacred hills of south-eastern Taiwan. A few elders in a neighbouring village claim to be their progeny, and they may be right, but their claim has yet to be verified.

Whatever the historical truth turns out to be, that day was an encounter with destiny. In my heart, I believe I am an avatar of the wise man Sakinu of the village in the forgotten alpine forest. The mixed feelings I had the moment I left the village and the tears I shed are fresh in my memory. I can see clearly each face and each waving hand, along with images from their lives and myself as a very old man. I am certain that the people of that clan have been helping me and guiding me and will continue to do so until I die.

The Harvest Festival

I felt so moved on the evening of the harvest festival. It had finally come to pass. I had witnessed all of the people in the village carrying out the Paiwan rituals and identifying as Paiwan.

Circled by the ancestral spirits, people were, for the first time in a long while, singing their own songs, dancing their own dances, wearing their own costumes, and celebrating their own harvest ritual. I was proud to sing with them, to sing back what had been lost. While my father and his generation sang the songs that were popular when they were young, those songs that came in the wake of cultural and environmental change, the elders sang Paiwanese songs, which had seemed as distant as the peak of the mountain against the sky.

I remember one elder saying, "Ah, it's been so long since we sang together and danced and drank wine we brewed ourselves. Our songs are beautiful. Let us sing them together, sing them with gusto, to let our dead *VuVu* hear them and to let everyone know that we are called Kacalisiyan". Kacalisiyan means *people of the slopes* – it is the Paiwanese word for "indigenous".

One song that was sang brought my generation and my parents' generation closer than we had been for a long time. This is how the song went. The boy sang:

> *Let us sing a Kacalisiyan song and dance our dance,*
> *It's been so long, we'd gotten so far away.*
> *Let us join hands, well, the one by my side*
> *is the girl I loved many years ago.*
> *It reminds me of when I was young*
> *and we were falling in love.*

Then the girl sang:

> *Now we are all old*
> *and we are the ina and kama of many children.*
> *It has been such a long time*
> *and my loved one still cherishes me.*
> *Let us sing together and dance until the sun rises.*
> *Let the sun shine on us Kacalisiyan.*

That evening, I heard the sounds of Lalaoran village from fifty years before and stories that were like freeze frames of that era. I danced the dance steps of the ancestors. I kept moving slowly. For fifty years, we had forgotten ourselves.

Now we had the courage to tell other people who we are.

From when I was born, Paiwan blood has been flowing through my veins. But before I understood my own Paiwan culture, the harvest festival in my village – the upper village – had long been dominated by the Amis people in the lower village. For the longest time, the Paiwan people of Lalaoran have been dancing Amis dances and wearing Amis clothes at our harvest festival, just as they did at my wedding, having forgotten the beautiful songs that our ancestors handed down to us. And we had forgotten the one hundred pacer snake totem and the symbolism of the sun. But in my memory, I am certain I have never taken part in an Amis harvest festival. I knew that I was not Amis. I knew that I was Kacalisiyan.

Someday, I thought, *I want to dance a dance that belongs to my people and wear the clothes of a Paiwan warrior.* I waited over twenty years, but I managed to see the day. Now the Paiwan people of Lalaoran remember who they are. They have an identity that makes them feel at home in the world.

On the second night of the festival, just before it was going to end, the chief said, "That's how it should be. We are Paiwan, Kacalisiyan. We have our own songs and dances – we will continue this next year and the year after that. Let the next generation hear and see our Paiwan traditional culture and spirit."

Her declaration completed the awakening of the Paiwan of Lalaoran, who had been in cultural hibernation for half a century. I believe everyone felt it. If we do not keep working hard, what will we have to hand down to let our sons and daughters know they are Paiwan?

So said an eighty-year-old fellow from the lower village to several Paiwan in the upper village: "To stumble and then to stand up again, that is such a difficult thing to do. I am so glad you Paiwan in the upper village are standing on your own two feet. This time you are united. You are a great people. Last night you sang your old Paiwanese songs – I felt so moved and shed tears, really. The fire you burned was so bright and high. I am sure your ancestral spirits and dead friends and relatives saw how hard you were trying. I am really happy for you, and I believe that you will go from strength to strength."

Actually, he is a Paiwan, too, from up the road in Tjavuali. He married into the lower village, which is Amis. Since his wedding day, he has been living the life of an Amis, but he still remembers the time before he got married, when he grew up Paiwan. He said the songs we sang reminded him of who he used to be. The clothes we wore recalled to him his ancestors and traditional Paiwan society. The old guy said, "I'm so old now, and it's enough for me to hear songs that belong to me. I am happy that after half a lifetime with the Amis, I have not forgotten I am Paiwan."

This is what I said to the Paiwan who attended the meeting of the upper village: "Our name is Paiwan – we have our own culture. We are not Amis. Why should we take part in other people's rituals? Why would we dance other people's dances? We even wear Amis clothes for the style. Let me emphasize again: we are Paiwan, and this cannot be changed. We have our own beautiful culture. And anyway, each culture has its own beauty. It's not a question of which is more beautiful, it's a question of who we are. Style shouldn't be a reason to sacrifice any aspect of culture. Though we have lost a lot of things, if we work hard we can find them again. One day we will see our children and grandchildren singing our songs and dancing our dances and wearing Paiwan clothes. Won't it be worth it? Wouldn't that be a beautiful thing? Think about it, Paiwan now, Paiwan forever. This is a fact that won't change."

An elder in the village replied. "Right, we are Paiwan. We should act like it."

Lalaoran was originally a Paiwan place. In the Japanese colonial era, Amis from the rift valley to the north relocated here in great numbers. I only found out doing oral history in the village. My grandfather once told the chief, "If we let Amis live here in Lalaoran, one day there will not be enough land to go around."

The chief fifty years ago would not listen. He was thinking of the boost in rental income he would get with all the extra people. And fifty years later everything my grandfather prophesied has come to pass. We have suffered a land loss and a cultural invasion, not just because of the Amis but also due to reform by different regimes. The Paiwan class system has collapsed, and the Paiwan chief no longer has the support of the Amis tenants. The culture has been breached with the invasion of foreign religion. The chief has lost everything. We have lost much – the restraining guidance of tradition, including the tradition of the institution of chief. What is the chief supposed to do when people do not respect her or the system she represents?

I am sure the elders know best how the culture has disintegrated. They have seen the whole process, from the time when we had everything to now, when we have nothing. And the chief feels most keenly the loss of the class system. But in my identity and belief, the Paiwan are a people with a chiefly system, and the chief is still the chief. The Paiwan system will not change – that is my faith.

From the moment the system began to disintegrate, along with related rituals, the Paiwan of Lalaoran lost their traditional restraint. The chief lost his or her power. In the past, if the Amis in the lower village had any insoluble disagreement, or if they were going to carry out a ritual, they had to inform the chief of the upper village. But at some point, the Amis selected their own chief and no longer informed the Paiwan chief of the upper village.

We Paiwan assumed that change was progress, and as a result our culture was steadily replaced by outside culture. Surprisingly, the Amis of the lower village had a cultural awakening. They came together out of their wandering and realized the preciousness of what they had lost. That was good for them, not so good for us. They became a hegemonic culture. From the 1960s on, they have re-inscribed the village and environs, made it Amis. Culturally, they have displaced the Paiwan, the people who had lived here for generations before they came.

I noticed many times how helpless and unwilling our chief appeared when she attended Amis harvest rituals in the lower village. The chief once said, in self-reproach, "Our culture's disappearance is my responsibility because I did not lead my people. I don't know how to explain myself to the ancestors. My dream is to see the Paiwan of Lalaoran find their culture again, but I don't know how to make this dream come true."

As a result of our ignorance and lack of identity, we sang other people's songs and danced other people's dances. For two decades, we covered our Paiwan appearances with Amis clothes. Finally, on 20 July 1996, at the harvest festival I sang Paiwanese songs at the top of my lungs to wake up all the Paiwan in the village, and I danced our ancestral dances to recover everything we had lost. Finally, we stood up. Bravely we came out of the shadows, proudly we could be ourselves, no longer under the influence of other groups. We are proud of our beautiful Paiwan culture. Though this is the first time, we will work hard to play our part, to tell the world that Lalaoran is a place the Paiwan have lived in for generations.

Before identifying with our culture, I too forgot who I was, and now I sang with a voice like a mountain – I sang loud. And I joined hands with my fellow villagers, no matter what religion, family, or class, whether they be commoner or aristocrat. That harvest festival, we danced our way to the realization that what was lost can be found again, that it is an unchangeable fact that we are Paiwan.

We may not have done the best job this year, but next year and in years to come the culture of the Paiwan of Lalaoran will be the pride of the Paqaluqalu, the Paiwan of eastern Taiwan. The fire burned brightly the evening of the harvest festival.

When it was all over, the chief said, "The ancestral spirits came to be with us. They were moved to see us come together once again and restore our culture in our homeland. We will continue to let other people know that Lalaoran is Paiwan, that Paiwan is Paiwan."

The villagers responded, "Yes, we are Paiwan, now and forever!"

That's how it happened, how the Paiwan of Lalaoran came together and sang with the long-lost voice of the ancestors. It was a restoration and an education.

My Name is Paiwan

On the eve of my wedding, when I told my father, a pious Christian, how we were going to conduct the ceremony, it turned out we did not see eye to eye. My father was adamant that we have a Christian wedding. But I was unwilling, no way. Now, I was committed to my Paiwan identity.

It wasn't always this way. Once upon a time, I was barely aware Paiwan blood flowed through my veins. I didn't know the influence our traditional culture would one day have on me. I never imagined I would go on to search for my heritage in our mythical stories. But I did. I had a cultural awakening.

From that time, I clearly understood I am Paiwan, a child of the sun. The hundred pacer snake is my protector. The oral history research I did taught me the story of where the Paiwan people came from, the story Paiwan parents used to tell their children, generation after generation. I believe before the Christian God came to this land my ancestors were here.

So I was certain that if my wedding were done in the traditional way, I would be blessed by the ancestral spirits.

To realize my dream of a traditional wedding, I spent three years gathering materials about traditional wedding garments and comparing them with what the elders in the village described. I arranged, prepared, and had custom-made the garments and ornaments that would adorn us. This was a dream my wife and I both wanted to realize: to restore the village's concept of a traditional wedding. It was such a long preparation – we really made a great effort.

But my father was unimpressed. "Why do you have to have a traditional wedding? It's too much trouble. What's wrong with a simple ceremony at the church? With Jesus to bear witness, you will be blessed." That was all he said.

I didn't say a thing. It was like there were ants crawling in my heart, biting me. "I am Paiwan, this is a fact that won't change," I said.

I never anticipated his reply. "Alright, you go be your kind of Paiwan. But know this, the traditional wedding ceremony you want to use is no longer practiced – nobody remembers. A few elders remember the ceremony we Paqaluqalu once used. But that's not the kind of ceremony you want to have."

I took a sharp breath and replied with greater certainty. "I am Paiwan. This is a fact that won't change!"

We Paqaluqalu – Paiwan people who moved from south-western Taiwan to the south-east coast – were under the influence of the Puyuma for a long time. In recent times, we endured the cultural oppression of the Amis. And we have been infiltrated by Han culture and Christianity. We

Paqaluqalu – especially the ones who live in Lalaoran village – have changed a lot. We have lost a lot of things. We face so many contradictions and struggles – we have forgotten too many precious things! Once, tradition taught people to practice restraint. But now, traditional culture has been phased out. It has disappeared. We have forgotten ourselves.

But I can't believe that the power of the Christian religion, or any of the other influences, can totally change all the culture in a Paqaluqalu person. To think my father would throw everything away, everything that belonged to Paiwan in the past. The change in the environment must have blurred his sense of self, not erased it.

Hoping to convince him, I said some words in defence of my choice of ceremony, which was part of a larger effort to restore a lost Paiwan tradition, which to me was the biggest task of all. But before I could get to the point, he interrupted me.

"The ceremony you're planning on using," he said, "is from Pingtung, it's not Paqaluqalu!"

Hot-headed, I replied, "What, are we supposed to use a Puyuma wedding ceremony? Or an Amis ceremony? Or a ceremony from some other indigenous tribe? Or perhaps I should wear a suit and tie, and she a white wedding dress?" I stopped and tried to calm myself down. Keeping my voice down, I said, "Times are changing and distances diminishing. In the past, geography made a trip to Mount Kavulungan a trek of several days. No wonder we Paiwan who moved to the east coast would start to change. The differences are understandable. But it was us who changed under Puyuma and Amis influence. The folks in Kavulungan continue living in the traditional way. They have preserved lots of traditions.

"And then the Christian God came, which was all well and good. I know how important he is to you. But I don't understand why we have allowed God to replace our ancestral spirits, and Bible stories our myths. Is God really so jealous? Can't we agree to coexist? You learned from the missionaries – why can't you let me learn from the people of Kavulungan? Why can't we combine the good things the people of Kavulungan are doing with the practices we have preserved in Paqaluqalu. That would be the best of both worlds. That would be a true eastern Paiwan culture."

My stubborn father did not think much of my justification. In the end, he said, "Alright, you go be your own kind of Paiwan!"

I was shocked. Had my father completely given up his faith in Paiwan? I could not believe he would say such a thing to me. *You go be your own kind of Paiwan?* That really hurt.

But that wasn't all. My father's response contained too many thou shalt nots, and his objections were unreasonable. He also objected to my emphasis on the chief. I had asked the chief to preside over the ceremony and to adorn us with the ornaments and feathers that symbolize status and pride. This was so very important to me. I wanted to highlight the fact that the Paiwan are a chiefly people and that the continuity of the chiefly institution represents the strength and health of Paiwan culture. But from my father's religious outlook, you cannot accept any heterodox beliefs. In the past at Paiwan weddings, the chief would ask the dead ancestors to come back and attend the wedding and give their blessings. My father said, "That's sorcery." He said it was a *palisi*, a Paiwanese word for ceremony, which had become a dirty word ever since the church came to town.

And that wasn't the worst. This is how my father cursed his child: "If you insist on carrying out a traditional wedding, one day you will have a child without hands or feet. Don't blame me, I've warned you."

My own father! How could he? Did he think I was betraying him? Or his Christian religion? My father used his Christian ideology to reject the traditional things his ancestors had bequeathed to him, and his religious consciousness told him that belief in a different faith would bring punishment upon us. He believed my determination was a refusal to bear witness to God. Fine, but what a thing for a father to say to his own son.

Getting married was in itself a simple thing, but religious and cultural conflict had made it complex. In my father's mind, there was only Jesus. He was the one true God. Other faiths were satanic.

My wife sat to the side crying. "Why would Father say that?" she asked.

I did not speak. There was too much to explain. It was too complicated. I could only say, "The ancestors will see all the things we are doing for Paiwan, and I believe that time will prove us right."

My wife wiped away the tears and told me, "I think your father will come 'round, eventually."

After forty years, it was time to revive the Paiwan wedding

ceremony. This required deep erudition and the courage of commitment. It marked a new beginning. One traditional wedding might remind the people in the village who they are. By experiencing it for themselves, they will understand, and future generations of Paiwan people will know what a Paiwan wedding is all about and many other things.

For instance, they now know the right way to dance. The afternoon of the wedding we danced the traditional dance. When we first danced, some people replaced Paiwan steps with Amis steps. They were dancing the Amis style of dance, moving their hands around and swaying their hips. They were even wearing Amis clothes! I didn't get it. Why would we want to dance the dances of other tribes? Angry, I yelled, "Hello, people! This is a Paiwan wedding, not an Amis wedding. Please dance in the Paiwan style."

Having said that, I was more conflicted than angry. I could hardly blame them because the Paiwan people of Lalaoran have had a weak cultural consciousness for a long time. For a long time, we Paiwan in the upper village have been dominated by the Amis in the lower village. The day of the wedding, people danced an Amis dance not on purpose but out of ignorance. I believe that our hard work and determination on our wedding day has had an impact, that time will prove that we Paqaluqalu Paiwan can stand up again and live in our own culture.

For me and all my tribespeople and the village, 29 March was the date on which, for the first time in forty years, we got back a bit of the culture we had lost. I believe many people were impressed by the ornaments and the ritual. Many cried. Elders said, "Sakinu, seeing you get married gave me a glimpse of the way we used to live."

And young people, living at a time when traditional culture has disappeared and modern culture has stolen in, felt that my wedding was new and stylish. "Brother, when I grow up, I want to get married the same way as you." That's what a kid in the village said to me. He sounded sincere, and I was touched. It gave me a lot of encouragement. That's what I wanted, for the next generation to accept their culture, so they wouldn't take it lightly or reject it. After the seeds of culture are scattered in young hearts, they will sprout and grow, drawing sustenance from the environment. Once that happens, nothing outside will be able to sway the identity in people's hearts.

The thing that moved me the most on my wedding day was in the evening when, having no more time for my father's objections, I went to ask the chief to dance with us. The chief was glad to. "It's been a long time," she said. "I haven't been so happy in a long time. Turns out my people have not forgotten their dances and songs." Crying now, she said, "Thank you, Sakinu."

The chief's joy made me feel proud, particularly because I could sense that my fellow villagers looked on the chief with newfound respect.

My Wife is Pingpu

Seven years after we met, my partner was trying hard to learn to be a Paiwan wife. I never asked her to do so and, in fact, demanded that she stop. I told her, "You can be Sakinu's wife, but you are a child of the Ancestor Ali." Ali is a Pingpu – plains indigenous – god.

After some thought and much struggle, she finally found an answer that satisfied her. "Husband," she told me, "I am willing to be your wife and live with you in your Paiwan village, but I have a request that when we have children, can we give them space, so they can find their own way of being Pingpu or Paiwan?"

I gladly assented. What right do I have to force the next generation to be children of the hundred pacer snake – the symbol of the Paiwan? If they tell me, "Father I want to be a child of Ali," I would gladly support them. And I would help them rebuild their lost Pingpu dwelling place in the depths of their hearts.

My wife's comment about our future children has made me reconsider the importance of ancestry. If it's our children's choice, and if it's my wife's choice, then identity is more important than ancestry.

When I was young, my grandfather said, "Whatever you do, when you grow up, don't marry a Pingpu girl. And not an Amis girl either."

I asked him why and he said, "Both Pingpu and Amis girls have teeth down there. They'll bite you on the *kutji*."

That threw me for a loop. I promised myself, *I must avoid either kind of girl to prevent my peepee from getting bitten off*. But the passage of time muddies all memory. I grew up. And I heard from my grandfather all the things that had happened to him in his life. Pingpu people pushed him out of the place where he grew up into a final pocket of Paiwan territory, which he was later forced to share with Amis people, who ate away at our territorial inheritance and nibbled away at our cultural heritage. I came to understand why my grandfather said what he did. A word like "conflicted" could hardly explain the feeling he had towards the Pingpu and the Amis, when he was forced to leave his land and feel like there was nowhere in the world where he could just be Paiwan.

I broke my promise. I fell in love with a girl from the plains. That created a potential problem. When I brought her home, would Grandpa be reminded of the Pingpu people who forced him from his land? Imagine my relief when he laughed and said, "Nice, very pretty. Her ass is big, she'll be able to bear your children. Her boobies are nice and big and will give lots of milk, so your kids will have enough to eat. They'll be healthy."

When he smiled, he showed his toothless gums. Then he asked me, "So is she Paiwan?"

Here goes, I thought. "Nope, she's Pingpu."

"Can she speak our language?"

"Jeez, Grandpa, the Pingpu can't even speak their own language, if they even admit that they are Pingpu. Often, they don't even know they are Pingpu. And you're asking if she can speak Paiwanese?"

"Then can she speak her own language?"

"Grandpa, nobody speaks Pingpu, it's a language that's gone to sleep."

So I don't blame my wife for not being able to speak her language. I don't blame the Pingpu for pushing my grandpa off his land. The Pingpu had to move, too. It wasn't their fault. The problem was an invasion of chauvinist Chinese immigrants, who managed to persuade Pingpu people they weren't good enough and Chinese culture was better. Not to mention that Chinese people didn't just occupy Pingpu land, they also oppressed them and cheated them. My Pingpu wife has never complained. But she knows that her people were the first indigenous people on the island to have to sacrifice their land and their culture. And that's just wrong.

One time, when we were talking about ethnic history and cultural problems, she said, "If only I could go back in time a hundred years and tell the Pingpu what I know, what I've seen, so that they would not get carried away in the flood of history. So they could hide from the Chinese and not fall for their tricks, so they can become the true masters of the plain, the eternal hunters of the deer!"

I didn't know if my grandfather understood what I had told him about her being Pingpu and all. I thought he had not heard me, but I was wrong. He told me a story.

"When we Paiwan were still living in the mountains," he said, "there were Pingpu villages on the plain. At the time we called them the 'people who run like river deer'. One day, all the men in the village went out hunting. While they were gone, there was a great crack of thunder. But there was no rain or lightning. When they came back from hunting, all the buildings in the village had burned down, and all women and children had been roasted alive. They were devastated. And they asked us Paiwan to help them with the burial ceremony. Our chief gave them food and millet seeds, and they went away, never to be seen again. I've heard elders say they left because too many people had died, and they were afraid that *akuma* would make trouble. They had to move somewhere else, never to return to their old home.

"Another time, lots of people came from Takao on the other side of the mountains. Afraid that they were on the war path, our chief waited in the road and asked them what they were doing. They said they were just fleeing the *pailang*, the bad (*pai*) men (*lang*), a Taiwanese loanword in Mandarin, and were just trying to find a place to live. They called themselves Pingpu. My grandfather said they were smart and had learned a lot of lessons from the *pailang*. Every man had a gun. Our chief let them come to our village. Some of them could even speak Paiwanese. They told me they had learned it from the Paiwan in the west. The chief wanted them to stay in our village, but the elders of the village advised against it. They told the chief, 'One day they will become more and more numerous, like the *pailang* they spoke of in the west, and they will want some of our land.' The chief sadly told them they could not stay. Nobody knows where those people went."

My grandfather's story showed he sympathized and approved of my wife's ancestry. I was thinking, *At least he's heard of them quite a bit.* Some people in this land have lived here a long time without knowing about the Pingpu. My grandfather's toothless smile told me my worry was for naught.

The moment I saw her seven years ago, I asked, "Are you a hillbilly?"

"No!" was her startled reply.

I was thinking, *As if you're not! You're so dark and your eyes are so big. Are you lying to me? You're indigenous, right, you just don't dare to let people know?*

Lots of indigenous people now are afraid people will find out they are indigenous. Like being an indigenous, being from the mountains, is shameful – like it's an unsightly physical feature you would want to hide.

Then I asked her, "So where're you from?"

She was from Hsintien, a suburb of Taipei. I thought of the road from Hsintien south through the hills to Wulai, where the Atayal live. Was she Atayal? To find out, I asked her, "Where do your grandmother and grandfather live?"

"Paternal? West of Tainan."

In south-western Taiwan? Wow! That was not what I was expecting. That was a very Taiwanese, or should I say not a very indigenous, part of the island. It felt like we were jumping around on the map. I was wondering, *Are there mountain folk in Tainan?* So I kept asking, hoping to find a bit of indigenous ancestry in her. "What about your mom?" Her mom was from Chinshan, north of Taipei, the northernmost place on the island. There aren't any indigenous people living there.

But with her dark skin and big eyes, she was of mountain-folk stock, make no mistake. Why was there not a whittle of indigeneity in her story? I looked into her big eyes, confused. There was something I could not ask – was she a child a couple from the mountains did not want? Or were her birth parents unable to take care of her and had to give her away?

After I had known her a while, she too wondered, "Am I 'mountain'? If I am, what group do I belong to? If I am not, why do I look so much like one?" All of this was a mystery to her. Her parents couldn't help her solve the mystery.

But when asked, her paternal grandmother told her, "Yes, I'm a savage, but I don't know which kind." Her grandmother and grandfather both look mountain. Finally, research gave her an answer. She was descended from one of the "mountain" peoples that once lived on Taiwan's western plains, the Pingpu.

She kept digging, deeper and deeper, to find her ethnic roots. Turned out those roots had gone dormant, but they hadn't died. Today if someone asks whether she's mountain, she can proudly say, "Yes, I belong to one of the Pingpu tribes." Which one? Now she knows. She is Siraya.

You have the right to know your roots, no matter who you are, no matter what has happened to hide your ethnic history from you. If you don't know who you are and you have a child and they ask you, don't they have the right to know? If you can't tell them, they have the right to go find out, like my wife did. With her big eyes and dark skin, she knew, those were clues. We followed up by visiting Toushe, the place to the west of Tainan where she grew up. When I saw the people there, I was amazed. They were mountain, no mistake. So why were they speaking Taiwanese?

Besides the way the people look, there's little sign of anything indigenous in Toushe, apart from the place where the Ancestor Ali sleeps – the public temple – which has an archive. We went through the records and became convinced that she was a child of the deer chasers, the Siraya. We took a long vacation in Toushe to do her family tree. I was as committed to finishing it as she. It felt like they were getting closer and closer, her ancestors. It turned out my wife is half-Pingpu on her father's side.

She said, "I may not have hands that are skilled at weaving because of the way I grew up, but I can still say I am proud to be a deer chaser, the progeny of the true masters of the western plains."

It's been seven years! I've followed my wife on dates that are not as romantic as your typical date. Or as relaxing. We don't have trendy clothes to wear. She goes with me to do things traditional Paiwan women did. Her beautiful hands have grown rough, and she is not quite as plump as she once was. But she never complains – she's gotten used to it. When you're the true master of the plains, you can get used to anything.

When she asked me if our children could have a space to decide for themselves how to be Paiwan or Pingpu, I said yes immediately. Whatever she wants. The Siraya were apparently matriarchal.

I still recall visiting her grandmother in her old house in Toushe a few years ago. It was made of bamboo. It was dilapidated, almost falling down. There wasn't another house like it. But to her grandmother it was comfy.

"Your boyfriend is a savage, isn't he?" her grandma asked her. She seemed happy to see me. "Savage, just like me."

"I'm from Toushe, born and bred," she told me in Taiwanese. "We used to join hands and dance and sing on Ancestor Ali's birthday, you know." Age has not worn away her memory, not at all. "I'm savage," she said, "not Han Chinese. I don't want to be Han Chinese."

Grandma's words keep echoing in my heart. If she can say she is proud to be savage, then so can I, so can my wife. Our children will be born in a few years. To commemorate our search for the footsteps of the Pingpu, me and my wife decided to call our first son Deer Chaser and our first daughter Siraya to let them know who their ancestors were.

honfordstar.com